Come to Shanta Bhawan!

Illustrated by WILLIAM M. HUTCHINSON
friendship press new york

Come to Shanta Bhawan!

by ALICE COBB

LIBRARY OF CONGRESS CATALOG CARD NUMBER: 63-8689

Printed in the United States of America

In grateful acknowledgement of Jonathan Lindell's help
in writing this book

Contents

1. *Eastward Ho!*

MY MOTHER SAYS SOMEDAY SHE'S GOING TO KNOCK OFF PACKing suitcases for a few days and write a book. She's going to call it *I Married a News Analyst,* with a subtitle, "No Such Place as Home."

That's because my father is always being sent off to places where big news is happening. I'd always wanted to go with Dad, but I'd given up, because there's always school. Once in a while Mother goes along, but not often, because she has an office in the church woman's society that keeps her busy most of the time—not to mention a son, David Conklin Brown, Jr. That's me.

This is all leading up to the subject of why a trip to the Orient, six weeks right in the middle of spring, was the kind of thing I used to dream about, but never believed would really happen. To make a long story short, it was on a March Friday afternoon that I got home from school and found Dad there early for a change.

I said, "Hi, pleased to meet you." And he said, "Hi, how about you and me visiting Katmandu?"

"Sure," I said. "Right after supper?"

"In about six weeks," he answered. "Two months at the outside. Do you think that you'll be able to fit it in your schedule?"

I still thought he was kidding. But when I looked at Mother and saw that here-we-go-again look in her eyes—well, I dropped down on the couch and pretended to go into a swoon.

"You can't *do* this to me!" I moaned.

Mother said, "Ssst! Poor lamb!"

Dad didn't even look.

"What kind of a life is this," I went on, "for a growing boy? A helpless victim of the flying machine era, that's what I am!"

Dad said, "Victim, my eye! The only thing that grieves you, Sad Sack, is the possibility of getting left *out* of a trip!"

"Who, by the way," I asked him then, "is this Katmandu you mentioned?"

Dad pointed to the atlas on the shelf. I dragged it down,

looked up Katmandu in the back, and started on my homework.

"For your information," I said, "Katmandu is a city. It's the capital city of Nepal. What country is Nepal a part of, Dad?"

"For your information," he said, "Nepal is not a part of any country. It is an independent country—a kingdom—all by itself."

"Yeah, here it is," I interrupted. "Sandwiched right in between India and Tibet. Why don't we go to Lhasa, Dad? What's ever happened in Nepal?"

"If you had read your father's excellent column not so long ago, you'd know what's happened in Nepal," Mother put in.

"I'm careful about my reading habits," I said. "But isn't this Nepal the place where that guy climbed. . . ."

"Everest," Dad supplied. "That's right, but there were two guys."

"Wow!" I really got excited then. "Things begin to click. Hillary and Ten—how do you say it?"

"Tensing," Dad said. "Tensing Norkey. They call him 'Tiger of the Snows.' "

"Yippee!" I yelled. "Himalayas, here we come!" And then to Mother, "Too bad mountain climbing is men's work. You'll probably get lonesome back here!"

Mother pretended to heave a big sigh. "Maybe I can bear it," she said, "if you send me a post card now and then!"

"No kidding, Mum," I said, "why can't you go, too? Does it cost too much?"

"Partly," she said. "But I've got other reasons—a little trip of my own to take to the Montreal woman's society meeting. And besides, your father and I think it will be a good idea for you two to travel together on this assignment."

Of course, when Mother says, "Your father and I" in a certain tone of voice, that settles the whole business. But I did wish she could go. Dad says that someday our family is going to get together and stay put, but meanwhile maybe we enjoy the times when we can be together more because so often we have to divide up.

The first thing after that was shots. I had to take tetanus, typhoid, cholera, and smallpox. I didn't mind them at all; but as Dad said, that's because I'm young and healthy. He only had to take cholera, but it made him awfully crabby even so.

Anyway, while Dad was fixing up visas and plane reservations and arranging for me to have a leave of absence from school, I dug in and tried to find out something about Nepal. Except for Everest and the Abominable Snowman, and Annapurna, I didn't know a thing. I read *Tiger of the Snows,* Tensing's book about the expedition up Everest, and so did Mother. After she'd finished she said she didn't want to hear of *me* trying anything like that, but the expedition was exciting to read about.

I kept telling the folks, whenever I could get them to

listen, little items I thought they ought to know. Dad was rather cross, on account of his shots, but Mother was reasonable, though not exactly what you'd call begging for information.

"Nepal," I read to her one afternoon, "500 miles long, 90 to 150 miles wide . . . 54,000 square miles altogether . . . snow-clad peaks 16,000 feet to over 29,000 feet. . . . Nepal, last homeland of mystery, closed country until 1951 . . . Shangri-La . . . Ran—Ranar—Ranarchy—" That one stopped me. "Do you know what 'Ranarchy' means?" I asked Mother.

"Heavens no!" she told me. "And if you think it's more important than tonight's dinner, I'll stop right now and we'll get on with our geography lesson. But your father won't like it."

"Ranarchy," I told her, "is the term used by 'insiders' in Nepal to describe their last hundred years of history. It's derived from the Rana family who were the hereditary prime ministers. The real kings were sort of like prisoners all this time. Nepal had a revolution in 1950, and the king and some political leaders kicked out the whole Rana family, and from that time on the doors have been open to the West. Gee-oh!"

"You don't say!"

"Yes, and do you know it's only ten years since the first Westerner actually began living there. Now things are changing like crazy, and there are even missionaries helping with hospitals and community centers and. . . ."

Well, Mother couldn't resist after I mentioned missionaries! She dropped the whole idea of supper, and we got down to serious study.

She got out some church papers telling where there is a brand new community service place. There was even a little map.

"Only a quarter of an inch from Katmandu!" she said. "Imagine! You've just *got* to go there and find out what they're doing, Dave! This is where we're sending our missionary money this year, and it's important!"

We didn't have a chance to see what Dad would say when he found Nepal instead of pork and beans for supper. Dad called just about that time to say there was a man he had to meet at the airport. He said we'd better go along, too, and have dinner with him and this man, who, Dad said, was a missionary leaving for *Nepal!*

"Now isn't it just like your father, to find someone like that!" Mother exclaimed. "This is really your chance to learn something!"

"We've been learning something for two weeks," I reminded her. "Is he a preacher?"

She didn't know, and she didn't know how old he was, either. My guess was he couldn't be too young, if he was a missionary. By the time we got to the airport, I had Mr. Kingston, the missionary, all built up with whiskers and maybe some kind of odd Nepalese outfit. And, of course, I thought he'd be carrying a Bible.

Anyway, when we got to the place where they were waiting for us, in front of the Cloud Room, and Dad introduced us to this young fellow, I was—well, let's say I was surprised! He looked like somebody you'd want on your team, for one thing. And he wore a suit like Dad's, maybe a little newer looking—nothing foreign about him that I could see.

I must have acted dazed. Dad sort of grinned, but he didn't say anything until the waiter had taken us over to a table by the window, and we were settled and had ordered. (Mr. Kingston ordered steak and potatoes, just like anybody else!) Finally Dad looked over at me and said, "What's the matter, Dave? Doesn't the gentleman from Nepal look the way you expected him to?"

"Well—no," I admitted, "not exactly."

Mr. Kingston laughed.

"David probably expected to see the gentleman from Nepal wearing a tarboosh—or maybe with a ring in his nose!" he said.

We all laughed then, and that helped to loosen us up a bit.

"It isn't that we haven't met any missionaries, Mr. Kingston," Mother fronted for me. "But they're usually at church, and—"

"And they always dress up in kimonos or saris or something," I interrupted.

Mr. Kingston said he made it a practice never to wear saris, (we all laughed again), but he said he did have a Gurkha outfit in his suitcase. He took an envelope out of his pocket and drew a picture, which he gave me. This is how it looked:

I noticed the knife right away, and asked about it. "Gee, do they carry things like that around nowadays?"

"The Gurkhas do, and they use them," he answered, "for practically everything, including cutting their nails. No Gurkha could get along very well without his kukri."

"Is it really true that Nepal is the roof of the world?" I asked him then.

"The highest mountain in the world is there," he said. "But there are some lowlands, too. Maybe the best way to describe Nepal is to say that it rises almost like steps." He began drawing again while all of us watched. For once I wasn't wondering when the steak would come.

"First, there's the bottom, or the strip of lowland, here on the south, lying right next to India. This bottom step is all low plain, very flat and hot and partly jungle. It's thickly populated, but a hard place to live in. You'll see the lowlands from the plane, but you probably will not stop there.

"The middle step is mountainous—the Midlands, they call it. And the next is called the Himalayas—high mountains, and directly beyond them is the highest step of all. The snowy peaks are the last level, and that's where you'll find Annapurna and Everest and the other famous mountains that the explorers are always trying to climb. But all up and down the sides of the mountains and in the tight valleys, the people from ages past have dug out innumerable terraced fields, where they raise crops. You'll see these terraces from your plane."

"Is Katmandu in one of these valleys?" Mother asked.

"In a very unusual one," he answered. "And that's interesting, too. You see, it used to be a lake, in ancient times, and after the water was drained away, people settled on the flat rich soil of the lake bottom.

"Now about Katmandu. There are three fairly large-sized cities in the Katmandu valley, and there are a good many villages, too. Katmandu is the largest city, and I think there are about 120,000 people living there. But—Katmandu—what a city!"

I heaved a big sigh just then, and Mr. Kingston smiled.

"You didn't expect a lecture, did you!" he exclaimed. But that wasn't what was the matter.

"I couldn't hold my breath any longer!" I said. "Tell us more about Katmandu!"

"You'll see it for yourself," he said. "Nobody can really talk to anybody about Katmandu. But I can tell you this, that right there in that little city, much smaller than Chicago or Buffalo or Toronto—right there is concentrated the wealth and culture of Nepal."

Dad broke the spell by getting down to business, which with him is international news.

"Katmandu is in one of the strategic areas of the world," he said to mother and me, "and Mr. Kingston's work is part of an important bridge between East and West. Of course, Nepal is neutral, right now."

"Nepal has been completely independent during its entire history," Mr. Kingston added. "This is probably because the doors of the country were kept so carefully closed for so long. But that day is over now. The look is toward openness, democracy, and development."

It made my head swim as he went on to tell us how fast things have happened. For instance, the very first airport was opened just six years ago, and now there are twelve landing places in the country. He said the U.S.A. and several other nations have embassies there, and are conducting technical aid missions. And he told us about a large hospital, Shanta Bhawan, in Katmandu that is run by missionaries.

"It's not easy to jump five hundred years in ten."

"But Nepal is pro-West, isn't it?" Mother asked.

"That's making it too simple," he answered. "Nepal is pro-Nepal. It is true that relations with the West are friendly now, and what happens in the next few years will be determined by how skillfully and honestly the West will keep its agreements with this fast developing country."

"And, of course, the United Mission to Nepal will have a part in this," Mother said.

"A very large part," Mr. Kingston agreed. "You know, I think, that this is an interdenominational program, and that we do not teach or preach Christianity directly, simply because that isn't permitted. We try to live Christianity by offering various services to the people of the country. We pray that our manner of life will witness to the gospel of Christ. I often think that the fact that there is so short a history of missions in Nepal, and the measure of restrictions placed upon them, have given us an entirely unique situation in which to work."

"What is so unique about it?" Mother asked.

"Two things in particular. The newness of work for missions has meant that most of them could unite right from the beginning and work as one body of Christians and one church. That is the unique feature of the United Mission to Nepal, you know. Many churches from different countries are all working together.

"The other factor, of restrictions on direct preaching, means that we have no full-time preachers among us. Instead, we are made up entirely of lay Christians. Our biggest concern is to learn how to truly follow our Master in a life of Christian service."

It was kind of a relief to me when the waiter came with the order, and Mr. Kingston said he certainly appreciated a good steak. He grinned at me.

"Steak is one thing we excel in over here," he said. "And, Dave, you'd better enjoy this one, because you won't get steak in Nepal. Of course," he added, "the Royal Hotel in Katmandu is set up for Western tourists now, so they'll do their best to please you. But my experience is that the harder they try to please Americans with 'Western' food, the more critical we are."

"I hope Dave will get outside the hotel a little," Dad said. "That's one of our problems—just how Dave can entertain himself in a strange city, while I'm shuttling back and forth to Delhi."

"He'll have no trouble at all," Mr. Kingston assured him. "The Nepalese are friendly, and you'll find the families of some of your newspaper colleagues most hospitable. And, of course, the mission hospital isn't so far away, either. It's too bad the Community Center, where I work, is so far off in the mountains, Dave, because you and my daughter,

Pat, would hit it off fine. She's about your age—she's fourteen. She'll be home on holiday from school at the time you're there. Anyway, you can prowl around the city all you like—it is perfectly safe anywhere, and the Nepalese will take you to their hearts."

"What do they eat in Nepal?" I asked.

Mr. Kingston smiled, and I certainly did like his smile. He looked as if he had a good time all the time.

"Pat calls it 'little pieces of things mixed up and a lot of pepper stirred in,' " he said. "Everything's hot, and you ought to go slow at first. When you get under the hotness to try to find out what you're eating, well, there's lots of rice. You always have that, every main meal. Rice and curry. The curry part is chopped up vegetables and sometimes meat and gravy. There's a kind of thick split-pea soup that my folks like to pour on the rice. And then, of course, good tea at the end of the meal. At the hotel, as I said, you'll have what they call American style food, but it won't taste like anything you have at home."

"That's what the Chinese kid at school said about the Chinese restaurants here," I put in. "He said the food wasn't really Chinese at all."

Then I asked him about the Nepalese kids, and he said I'd probably meet some boys right away.

"I'm not so sure about the girls," he said, "although you may get to know some of the educated and up-to-date families in the city. They are not so restricted by the old customs. A good many of the government people and newspapermen have traveled in Europe and in the States, too, and know our ways."

"What about school?" I asked him.

He said he thought we'd probably get there just when the school in Katmandu had its vacation.

"In a way, that's a pity," he said. "You could probably enter the international school for a few weeks, if it were in session. But in another way it's good because you'll have a chance to explore the city with some of the youngsters."

"And will I have to stay in Katmandu the whole time?" I asked.

"You see the truth is, David has extravagant ideas," Mother explained. "He's been reading about Tensing Norkey and Sir Edmund Hillary, and he's dying to get into the mountains."

"I have an ambition to see the Abominable Snowman, too," I added.

"And I'll be perfectly happy if he never gets within miles of that creature!" Mother laughed.

Mr. Kingston assured her that nobody so far had ever seen the Abominable Snowman, and he doubted if I would.

"But seriously," he went on, "I think we ought to find a way of getting David and his father both out into the hinterlands. I'll be back at the Community Center when you arrive and, of course, you'll be most welcome there. But it's a long trip—a good six days' hike through the mountains."

Dad shook his head. "Sounds great," he said, "but. . . ."

Mr. Kingston looked at his watch, and right then we heard his flight being called. He jumped up, grabbed my hand and then Mother's and Dad's.

"Tomorrow I'll be with my family in Katmandu, and the next day we'll trek through the mountains!" he exclaimed. "We'll lay out the red carpet at Ama Kmu, and hope you'll come. Thanks! Blessings! Bon voyage!"

He was out of there and down to the loading gate faster than any football tackle we've ever had at Northside High.

"Whee!" I said. "Off in a cloud of dust! He's some guy. I'm for Ama Kmu!"

"David, you must try to get to that center!" Mother said. "But be very careful!"

Dad and I both laughed. That's Mother. She wouldn't have me miss anything for the world!

* * *

And that was how it all started!

Looking back, it still seems as though all this couldn't have happened. But because it did happen, I'll never be the same person again. Mother says every minute and every experience of life make you a little different. I feel as though this one took me to live in another world for a little while, and whenever I read a newspaper now, or go to a movie, or to church, or even when I'm just walking down the street in Chicago to catch a bus—I'll have a different feeling about it. Dad says this is what it means to look at the world from Himalayan heights!

2. *A Strange Land and Friendly People*

TRAVELING BY JET IS EASIER TO DO THAN TO BELIEVE. WHEN you think of starting from Chicago, in the middle of the United States, and arriving at Delhi in India, which is practically exactly on the other side of the globe, a little over twenty-four hours later, it takes your breath away!

The thing that bothered me most was this business of time. My watch was always behind, and they kept saying over the loudspeaker to put it forward an hour, or maybe two hours, or three. It gave me the creeps to have time leaping along that way. And it seemed as if every few minutes they were bringing around another meal. It's not that anything's the matter with my appetite, but the problem was to get hungry for the right meal at the right time.

Some people are impressed a lot by the way you drop casually down into one country, and then into another one a few thousand miles farther along. I wasn't, though, because it seemed as though the airports all looked alike and most of them were full of American tourists. You really got to wondering if there could be anybody left back home because we all seemed to be in Rome or Paris.

But it was being "aloft," as the pilots say it, that really sent me. Dad felt the same way about it, he said. He kept reminding me that we were spanning oceans and continents at a height of 35,000 feet, and at a speed of 600 miles an hour.

"The miracle of flying through air is one of the most amazing achievements of man," he said. "One would be tempted to take pride in it, except for its smallness compared with the miracle of space in which we travel. Today we are just getting used to the idea of penetrating outer space. Tomorrow the universe. Yes, Dave, maybe in your lifetime—the universe!"

The big 707 jet landed us at Delhi, where we were to change to a DC-3 for Katmandu. We stood in line at the airport to have our passports examined by some very dark guys with beards and turbans. Dad said they were Sikhs, who never cut their hair, because of their religion. They looked so strange to me that I could hardly believe I was hearing them speak real English, English-English!

Otherwise, the Delhi airport was like all the others, with crowds of people and lots of noise. We got through the line about noon, and our plane to Katmandu was already on the runway, ready to take off. Dad said it was the quickest connection he'd ever made in Southern Asia.

The DC-3 wasn't any small crate, either, but it seemed small compared with the 707 jet we'd just gotten off. It wasn't long before I was wishing we were in an even smaller plane, because it seemed as though there wasn't much elbow room between those mountain peaks we weaved around.

Before that, though, we flew over the lowlands Mr. Kingston had drawn for us on the envelope. We could see the mountains ahead of us, and very soon our plane began to climb over them. We could feel ourselves going up-up-up and then over the first ridge, fairly scraping along the top. We must have crossed two or three ridges like that. One fellow said it was like looking down on several steep staircases, with their lower steps covered with shining glass. Dad said those glass shelves were rice paddies, made on terraces.

We came over the last ridge suddenly, and lo and behold there was the Katmandu Valley stretched out, looking like a round green plate with this high rim of peaks all around.

They say the descent into Katmandu is the most dramatic three minutes of flying time in the world, and I can believe it. You begin to circle down in a hurry, and while you're circling, over on the other side of the valley, you can see the peaks in rows and still higher rows until at the top they end in a rugged line of glittering snow, with clouds shifting around so now you see the glitter and now you don't. The closer peaks looked to me like some of these modern sculptures that are all points and angles. They seemed to be in a scramble, and yet you could feel how the whole design had been thought out line by line. I must have said that last thought out loud, because Dad answered me. "That's right, Dave," he said. "It certainly doesn't look careless!"

We came down in a hurry then, and that green plate now seemed more like the bottom of a bowl. The hills rimming it had taken on a purple look, and the green gave way to a mixture of red and white. Dad said they were temples and palaces.

Shangri-La! I thought. This is Shangri-La!

Then suddenly we were coming in right over green fields, practically shaving the tops of the trees, and at last rolling onto the landing strip. I drew a deep breath. Some trip!

There was a celebration at the airport, but it wasn't because we were anybody special. Dad said they always welcome people who come, and see them off when they go, in this part of the world. There were half a dozen fellows there, all newsmen. A couple were Nepalese, I guessed, although you couldn't tell by the way they dressed. One, an American, was the *New York Herald Tribune* man, and some of the others looked like Europeans. I thought of Mr.

Kingston, who must be miles away in the Himalayas by this time.

After landing there was some business of getting our passports looked over and stamped, going through customs, and getting a taxi (it was a jeep). Through all this I just followed along after Dad and the others, feeling a little dizzy and mixed up and not my usual, intelligent self, as I told Dad.

Maybe that was why the ride from the airport to the hotel, especially the part inside the city of Katmandu, was like a dream in technicolor, full of red and gold temples and small streets with carved balconies hanging over them, loaded with flowers. And crowds and crowds of people. The books had said that more than a hundred thousand people live in Katmandu, but I hadn't expected to see them all the first afternoon.

We went straight to the Royal Hotel, where most of the international visitors and all the newsmen stay. Dad likes small places, but he hadn't much choice this time, except to live in splendor, he said.

Splendor is the right word for the Royal. I took one dizzy look around the lobby and began to come alive. Dad must have noticed my eyes popping!

"You're not dreaming," he said. "This is one of the Rana palaces we're living in. Not much like home, is it?"

"I—I didn't know Nepal was so rich," I said finally.

"Nepal isn't rich," he said. "The Ranas had expensive tastes, and they had all the money. Things are different now. But why don't you have a look around here, while I take care of the business?"

Maybe I answered. Anyway, he went on over to the desk while I leaned up against a marble post there by the door to watch the passing scene and try to take it all in.

It was easy to believe we were in a palace. The floors were marble, I noticed, with big fur rugs made of skins from animals like bears, tigers, leopards, and others you would see in the zoo. It was like a magnificent hunting lodge that you might see in the movies. Around the walls there were big old carved chairs that Mother would have hated on account of the trouble of keeping them dusted. I suppose the porters took care of such things at the Royal. There were quite a few porters around, good looking fellows, all wearing what looked like long white dresses and little round hats.

The things that took my eye, though, were the elephant footstools. Each stool was made of one big elephant's foot with ivory toenails! I didn't dare put a foot on one, but it was fun to look at.

The ceiling looked miles high, and was painted gold and red in fancy designs and pictures. And those chandeliers! Each one must have weighed a ton. I hated to think what it would feel like to be directly underneath one should it take a notion to fall!

While I was standing there, a little kid came past me through the door and went stumbling around, begging in the lobby. He looked as if he were lost, but after a while I decided he must be blind, or practically blind, because his eyes were all squinted up. He certainly didn't belong in this swank hotel lobby, anyway.

At first nobody paid much attention to him, although one or two folks sort of brushed him off. It made me feel terrible to see him stumbling that way. The kid couldn't have been more than seven or eight.

I was trying to make up my mind to go over to the kid and see if I could talk to him at all. Then something happened that was nothing very special, and so simple it's hard to tell about, but it was the waking up moment for me in Nepal. What happened was that one of the porters noticed this boy finally, and went over to him. At that point I was just about to get into the act myself, because it looked as if the porter were going to throw the kid out into the street. But this was Nepal, not North America.

Of course, I hadn't the slightest idea what the porter said to the boy, but whatever it was, it was friendly. One word, or maybe words, especially seemed to be magic. The kid stopped crying. I heard the same words again and again as they talked. From the way that little boy's face lighted up, you'd have thought the porter had offered him a wonderful present or told him some good news. What struck me, though, was a feeling that those magic words were ones I'd heard before!

The kid went on outside then, and I saw him sitting on the ground, not far from the big door. He wasn't begging any more, although a good many people passed by. He was

just sitting, squatting rather, as they all do in Nepal, and waiting.

All this made me curious. Since the porter was standing there, with his eye on the boy, I decided to say something to him, on the chance he could understand English. (Dad says it's a funny thing that Americans all over the world expect everybody to speak English, while Americans very seldom speak anything else themselves!)

"What was it you said that made that boy look so happy?" I asked him.

Apparently he hadn't realized that I'd been watching, because he looked startled. Then he smiled. He did speak English.

"The boy is sick," he explained. "Sick and poor. I tell him the begging is no good. I tell him *come to Shanta Bhawan!* He does not know how. I tell him when I go away from this hotel, we come together. He waits. We will come to Shanta Bhawan."

"Shanta Bhawan. That's the word!" I exclaimed.

"Yes, yes, Shanta Bhawan!" He laughed as if he were real pleased. "Don't you know everybody sick comes to Shanta Bhawan?"

He went off to do something then, waving and smiling to me. I went on over to the desk where Dad was just finishing filling out all the cards and forms.

"You'll get your passport back later," he said. "And if you'd like to get some money changed, this is the place to do it. Eight rupees to the dollar."

I signed a traveler's check for ten dollars and gave it to the desk clerk. He counted out a whole walletful of money in exchange.

"Wish I were really as rich as I feel right now," I said. Then I turned to Dad. "Do you know about a place here—Shanta Bhawan, I think it is?"

"Shanta Bhawan? Of course, it's the mission hospital here in Katmandu."

"And it was Mr. Kingston who told us about it!"

It clicked! Dad nodded.

I told him about the blind boy while we were walking upstairs. There are no elevators in Katmandu.

"Maybe what happened wasn't so important," I said. "But it sticks in my mind. Do you suppose we could see that Shanta Bhawan?"

"Of course," Dad said. "I'm writing the story—" he stopped suddenly and looked at me.

"Why don't you write it, Dave?" he said.

Sure enough he was serious! I nearly fell down the stairs.

"M-me?" I stammered. "For—for—"

"For my column," Dad said. "What do you say?"

I couldn't say anything, but Dad seemed to think it was all settled.

"You can have a by-line," he said. "The public will appreciate a change. And here, apparently, is our corner of the Rana castle."

The porter let us into the grandest room I'd ever seen, much less lived in. In fact, there were two rooms, both with those lofty ceilings and big fancy furniture. That much I saw, even with most of my mind on something else.

Dad's column! Me! What would Mother say?

As soon as the porter had gone, Dad turned to me again. "We'll go to Shanta Bhawan tomorrow," he said. "And tonight, if you can get your flying legs adjusted to land travel, and if I don't get held up at the news service, we'll steal a few hours for an excursion. O.K.?"

Tonight, an excursion with my dad around the magic city of Katmandu! Tomorrow, an assignment to write a story for Dad's column for the papers, and a chance to "come to Shanta Bhawan."

Everything was O.K. by me!

3. *Meet Marty Rosen*

I DIDN'T EVEN HEAR DAD LEAVE THE NEXT MORNING. BUT there was a note, telling me he'd be gone all morning and I was on my own. "Try to keep from taking wooden nickels, Punk!" thc note said. So here I was in a hotel, in Katmandu, in the middle of Nepal, in the middle of Southern Asia, not knowing a soul east of New York City!

I went over to look out of the window. Across the street and as far as I could see were tiers of roofs, mostly red, that reminded me of a honeycomb. The streets below were crowded with people walking along, and bicycles and jeeps weaving in and out among them. It struck me that nearly

everybody, women as well as men, was carrying a load. You didn't see them pushing carts or driving wagons. I remembered a place in Tensing's book where he said, "A Sherpa boy looks up at the mountain, and he looks down at a load," or something like that. Some of those loads were twice as big as the persons carrying them.

Four or five buildings in the neighborhood stood out above the others, like churches or temples. Almost as many temples as houses in Katmandu, Mr. Kingston had said. Nepalese must be religious people, sure enough! One of

the smaller temples had eyes painted on it. It would be interesting, I thought, to see how eyes like that would look on the churches at home!

That was quite a lot of looking before breakfast. It seemed as though Nepal was a place that could give you a good many ideas.

Down in the lobby I explored some more and especially noticed the rhinoceros head that stared down from over the door. I took some time to look at the portraits on the walls, fierce looking guys that I wouldn't want to get in an argument with on a dark night in a strange place. The clerk at the desk told me they were some of the Ranas, who had ruled for a hundred years and then had been ousted in the revolution. There were two big life-sized portraits, too, one of the King and one of the Queen. I remembered that the King's father had opened Nepal to the world and "started the clock," as Mr. Kingston had put it.

At this time of day there weren't many people in the lobby, but I did see two women wearing long black skirts with red borders. There were some tourists in Western clothes and several Nepalese men who had round high caps that they wore indoors as well as out. They seemed to be able to speak two languages, changing from Nepali or Hindi back to English without any trouble.

One of the porters noticed me and pointed to the dining room, so I went along to get my breakfast. The people in there seemed to be having bacon and eggs as per usual. In a way it might have been a dining room in any hotel at home, but there was a feeling about it that made you know you were in the Orient. It wasn't exactly how things looked, or sounded, or smelled even, but there was a difference.

While I was thinking about this, and wondering which one of the empty tables the waiter would lead me to, it was all taken care of. Somebody stood up across the room and waved. I saw it was a kid about my age.

"American," the waiter said. He led me right over there and laid down the menu with a flourish. This kid was all by himself, eating a grapefruit. Just like home.

"Hi!" he said. "New York or Chicago?"

"Chicago," I said. "How did you know?"

"Easy," he said. "Anybody can tell you're from the States, and Americans here are either from New York or Chicago," he said. "Funny, but that's the way it seems to be."

"How about you?" I asked.

"Me, I'm Canadian—Martin Rosen. Part of Toronto's municipal zoo."

I told the waiter I'd have grapefruit and bacon and eggs. When I told him my name, Martin was impressed, the way folks always are. It's because almost everybody knows my name from reading Dad's newspaper column.

"Gee! You aren't the famous one, are you?" he asked.

"No," I told him. "That's my dad. What do you mean about the zoo?"

"It's a joke," he explained. "Mom and Pop are ornithologists—that means bird collectors—and I figure, being their son, I'm a sort of *rara avis* myself. That's Latin for 'rare bird.' I know quite a lot of Latin, because birds all have Latin names. Did you know that?"

I didn't, but it sounded interesting.

"My folks are famous, too," he said. "I mean they're sort of famous. You ought to see our collection."

"Gee, I'd like to," I said. "Collecting must keep them pretty busy."

"Sure does," he said. "They get out early. I don't, though. You see, I go to school most of the time, but right now school's out—we're on holidays. Guess your dad has got big business today, interviewing the King or somebody important?"

I didn't know about the King, but told Martin we were here for six weeks. He said he wished we were staying longer.

"I'm the only Canadian here, the only one in school, I mean. The rest of the kids in my class are all foreigners."

"You mean Germans, French, and like that?" I asked him.

"No, Nepalese," he said.

It sounded to me as if Marty Rosen were the foreigner, but I didn't say so.

"Is school like at home?" I asked then.

"Sort of," he told me. "They speak English, of course. Everybody wants to learn English now, here in Nepal."

"I was wondering if I'd meet any of the Nepalese kids, because somebody told me they're not always so anxious to have Westerners in their homes."

"Yeah, that's so, and it's easy to understand it," Marty said. "Why, this whole country was shut up like a jail until —well, until 1951. They hardly allowed anybody from outside to come in until then. Anyway," Marty went on, "everything's different now. More like back home. Some folks have a lot of company and some don't. But there's one kid at school I really like. I bet your dad would know Rama's father, too, because he's a writer for the *Katmandu Times*. That's a Western-slanted paper, by the way. I hear it gives the U.S. a lot of good write-ups. What are you doing today?"

"I thought I'd take a look around the city and visit some of those temples."

"Most of the folks here are either Hindus or Buddhists, or both," Marty said, "and they have a lot of temples and priests. They have certain things they don't eat, same as us, and everybody is some caste—high, low, or middle. Rama is a high caste Hindu. He's a Brahman."

"Certain things you don't eat?" I asked him.

"Yeah, that's the way it is in my religion," he said. "I'm Jewish. Reformed Jewish." He said no more about religion but went on to tell me about looking around the city. "You ought to go to the old part. That's where you buy things in the bazaars. But you oughtn't to go by yourself, though, because you have to know how to bargain. It's a game everybody plays. I guess I better go with you, or—say—"

"The old part?" I asked him. "It all looks old to me."

"No—this is the new part we're in now," he said. "I know somebody who can tell you how to find your way around. It's Rama, the kid I told you about. I'll let you know—"

He stopped then and waved to somebody at the door. I turned around to see.

"It's Mom and Pop," he explained. "They're back from bird watching, and I bet they found the one they were looking for. It's very rare."

Marty looked pleased to see them, and he started to jump up when he waved. Then, as soon as they started over to where we were, he sat down again and only sort of nodded his head, as if he were greeting an acquaintance. Maybe he wasn't so pleased after all!

But they were glad to see him all right. No doubt about that. And sure enough they had found that bird.

"Great morning!" Marty's father exclaimed. "Worth the whole rest of the year put together, and what a shot your mother got!"

"Shot?" I exclaimed out loud. You wouldn't think they'd have *shot* a valuable bird, I said to myself.

Then they noticed me. Marty's mother sort of threw back her head and laughed, the nicest laugh. They were both swell, I could see right away. Not a bit old or stuffy.

She held up the camera that was hanging around her neck by a long leather strap.

"*This* kind of shot!" she said, still laughing. "And how nice for Marty to have found a friend here at the hotel!"

"Glad the birds are biting," Marty said. "This is David Conklin Brown—" He stopped for half a second on purpose, to give them a chance to look surprised, then he added, "Junior. Dave's father is here to write all about Nepal for the papers."

Marty's folks wanted to talk to me about Dad, but all of a sudden Marty seemed to clam up. I couldn't understand what was the matter, because they were both so nice and friendly. It occurred to me that Canadians might be that way, so I wasn't a bit sorry when they all left the dining room and went upstairs.

After finishing my bacon and eggs (Mr. Kingston was right—they didn't taste like the ones at home), I strolled out into the lobby and asked the clerk at the desk for a newspaper. Then I noticed they were written in Nepali.

"No English papers," the clerk said, as if he hated to disappoint me. But he lightened up. "Wait—we have just the thing—an American newspaper!"

He dived under the desk and brought out a European edition of *The New York Times*. It was two weeks old, so I'd already read the front page news in the Chicago papers a long time back. But it was fun to read familiar news in different surroundings. There were some articles that made me feel a little homesick. One told about a cyclone in Texas, and another was about a fire we'd had in the Chicago Loop. There was even a short story from Colorado about somebody who claimed to have seen peculiar tracks in the snow and had started a story about an Abominable Snowman in the Rockies.

By this time I was beginning to feel blue. I went out for a walk around the part of town near the hotel, the part I'd been looking at from my window. Marty had called it the new part, but it didn't look very new to me. And even with all those people it seemed lonesome. I decided I'd wait to go walking with Marty. But on the way back to the hotel, I got to wondering if Marty would really come and if he would call that Hindu boy he'd mentioned. He certainly hadn't seemed very eager at the end of breakfast when his folks came.

The mail had come by the time I got back. There was a funny card from Mother, mailed before we left home, with a picture of an empty doghouse with a wide-open door. Down at the bottom it said, "Nobody home!" She meant that for a joke, of course, but it made me feel terrible.

On top of being homesick, I began to feel queasy, as if the grapefruit or something might be coming up. Finally I sat down on one of those carved chairs in the lobby, and just waited to see what would happen. Climbing up these stairs seemed too hard to bother about.

That was where Dad found me, with my feet propped on an elephant's foot, and no doubt looking green from the chin up. I didn't even know he was there until he spoke to me, and when I got my eyes open there seemed to be two of him.

Dad didn't say much, but he put a hand on my shoulder, and then I suddenly began to feel better. It seemed to take a long time, though, to get up to the suite. "Funny that I should feel sick," I muttered.

"It's not funny!" Dad said. "It's normal. Most everybody gets a little sick on his first trip, if it's only from getting used to new water."

I felt still better when I got stretched out on the bed and swallowed a nasty little brown pill Dad gave me. After that I began to feel myself drifting off to sleep, but I kept blinking so I could keep awake to tell Dad about things first. I told him about breakfast, and Marty, and the bird collectors. He was interested in that famous bird of theirs and made some notes for his column. He knew Rama, too —or rather he knew Rama's father.

"One of our best," he said. "And he and his family may be coming to the States next year."

"Do you think Marty is going to call Rama?" I explained about how he'd clammed up after his folks came.

"Of course, he'll call Rama," Dad assured me. "You'll hear from him tonight, or I'll miss my guess. And as for his clamming up—well, I'd say your friend is suffering from a slight case of absentee parents. So is David Conklin Brown, Junior—and I'm sorry for that, Dave!"

There was one other thing that bothered me. It was a struggle, but I finally managed to say, "Shanta—"

"Shanta Bhawan is out for today," he answered. "And so are you. But while you're going to sleep, Dave, try to remember that your folks think their son is a little bit of all right! You'll remember that, won't you, Dave?"

I don't remember answering, but I remember feeling good. A little homesick, but not so very. And good!

4. *The Old City and Some New Plans*

MARTY ROSEN CERTAINLY DID KEEP HIS PROMISE, AND DIDN'T lose any time about it, either. When Dad got back that night, he found a note stuck in our door. I woke up long enough to read it. It said Marty and I were to meet in the lobby early so we could meet Rama Prasad at the Arch by 8:00 A.M.

"What's the Arch?" I asked Dad. He said it was a sort of entrance way into the old city.

All this was the reason why, on our second morning in Nepal, it was I, instead of Dad, who rolled out early. In fact, I was down in front of the big door at 7:30, although it wasn't easy! Marty was waiting for me. He seemed the kind of fellow you'd find it hard to get ahead of!

"Well, we made it!" he said cheerfully. "I wouldn't have myself, except Mom and Pop always start out before daylight, and I told them to give me a shake."

I must have looked over toward the dining room right then, because Marty said, "Uh-uh," shook his head, and hurried us on out through the big door.

"Not this morning. Nobody, but nobody has breakfast in Nepal," he said as we made our way down the street. "I mean nobody who's really Nepalese. Maybe they have a cup of tea with buffalo milk, but they wait until about ten, and then have a soup-to-nuts. Anyway, we've got to get going—"

I *thought* he said "buffalo milk" but couldn't be sure, because Marty was hustling along ahead of me, and a good deal began to happen nearby. A long string of people came trotting down the street, carrying loads of firewood on their backs and huge baskets of fruit and vegetables. They seemed to be heading for market. But Marty wasn't about to let me look at the scenery, either.

"Come on, we're in a hurry," he said. "You have to get to market early, because if you're the first one in the morning to go into a shop, they've got to make a sale. Sometimes you can get something for practically nothing!"

It made me dizzy.

"Why do they have to make a sale?" I asked.

"It's because the first customer settles their luck for all

day. They've just got to sell you something, and they'll practically give it away to keep you from leaving without buying anything."

"Whether you want it or not?" I asked.

"Oh sure. The idea is they've got to sell you *something*. Say, look up there, will you! There's the good old Arch, and there's Rama waiting, I think!"

By this time, of course, we were quite a distance from the hotel. We had been sprinting along while Marty talked up all that storm. Right ahead of us was what looked like a high bridge stretched clear across the whole street. It had little walkways on either side.

"Yeah," he said now as we got up closer, "there's good old Rama, right on the dot!" He laughed. "And you know, that's something, because Orientals aren't ever supposed to get any place until an hour later!" He waved wildly and yelled, "Hi! Here we are—over here!"

The other people in the street turned around to look, too, but it was easy to pick out Rama as he left the walkway at one side of the Arch and started to meet us.

My first Nepalese acquaintance! One of these days, I thought, maybe I'll be able to say that I have a real full-blooded Nepalese for one of my close friends!

When he came up closer, Rama didn't look very dark, not much darker than Marty, in fact. But his eyes were different, black and sparkly, and his hair was shining black and a little curly. He acted quite formally at first, but Marty had warned me about that.

"Nepalese are really friendly," he said, "but the Hindus, especially Brahmans, are likely to be a little stiff when you first meet them. Rama's a good egg, though. He'll loosen up!"

"Hi!" Marty said again as we came close together. I noticed Marty wasn't the least bit the way he had been with his parents. "Here's my friend Dave Brown that I told you about. And, Dave, this is Rama Prasad."

For a split second both Rama and I stood there, wondering what to do. At that moment I remembered seeing people at the hotel put both hands together and raise them to their chin in greeting. It looked easy. I thought I'd better try it. But at the instant I began to put my hands together, Rama put out his right one for a Western shake. Then we both did a quick reverse, and he raised his hands while I stuck my hand out. That broke the ice. Marty was tickled.

"Dave," he exclaimed, "you'll never know how funny you looked!"

"No funnier than you, Martin, when *you* first tried the Nepalese greeting!" Rama exclaimed, and to me added reassuringly, "Martin looked very funny, indeed!"

We all laughed, then, including Marty, who was the best sport ever. Then Rama went on doing the honors.

"My father speaks highly of your parent," he said to me. That formal way of talking must have been catching, because I found myself answering the same way. "And my father speaks highly of *your* parent!"

Marty laughed again.

"This is just like acting in a play!" he remarked. "Hadn't we better travel on?"

But Rama wasn't quite ready to drop the formality.

"My mother," he began, "requests that both of you honor us by being our guests this morning, after the tour of the bazaars."

Imagine being invited into a Nepalese home so soon.

"Well, thanks!" I exclaimed. "That sounds great."

"Wait till you taste the pastries!" Marty said. "And the tea!"

"With buffalo milk?" I asked, and Rama nodded his head.

"Maybe," he admitted. "Or maybe cow's milk. We have many of the water buffalo in this country, and their milk is good."

Marty asked a bit impatiently, "Do we start now?"

"Now," Rama said, "through the Arch—and into the old city!" He took the lead, and Marty fell behind with me.

"It's a different world, Dave," he said in a low voice. "You've never seen anything like it before, in your whole life!"

A different world—and what a world! The old city of Katmandu made me think of a honeycomb again, with houses and temples, little ones and big, all packed in tightly together, and streets so narrow we could almost reach across them. Nearly all the brick houses seemed to be three to five stories high, with balconies. I judged the people generally live upstairs and do business on the street level floors.

What I noticed everywhere was the carving, all done by hand, and all the wooden pillars that stood in front of the houses. The windows looked as if they were framed with wooden lace.

Houses and palaces and temples were all mixed together helter skelter, and often the larger temples were built around an open square where all kinds of business was going busily on. Nuts, grains, vegetables, and fruits were for sale along street after street: papayas, pineapples, tangerines, mangoes, and the tiniest little bananas, about the size of your finger. And were those bananas ever sweet! I had to ask about the papayas, because they were new to me. Marty assured me we could have them for breakfast at the hotel any morning.

"There's nothing better anywhere than a good papaya, unless it's a good mango," he told me. "It's something to write home about, man!"

But there were lots of other things besides the fruits and vegetables and grains. There were sweets and cakes (I was to taste some of those later at Rama's house), and in some places cooking was going on right there where they were being sold. Right next to the bake shop you might see somebody selling leather stuff, or making clay pots on a stone wheel. Close by there might be some women combing one another's hair. Next you'd pass by a temple with a fierce-looking carved god, smudged over with what looked like red or orange colored powder or paint.

On one corner we saw a strange looking old fellow with long hair and not much clothing. He was squatting down on the street. On the pavement in front of him were several little brass saucers with things that looked like different colored powders, bright pieces of cloth, and colored strings. The old man was mixing them together, and all the time he was muttering or chanting something. Rama was surprised to see him. He said this was a holy man, and that they were usually around only on special days.

"Speaking of holy men, you ought to take a real good look at the temples," Marty said to me. "They're what Katmandu's especially famous for."

Rama nodded and said, "It is true we have many temples. The art of building temples is Nepalese, and wealth, physical strength, labor, and sometimes even the blood of human beings have gone into the making of these temples."

The temples were built in stories or tiers, with slanting roofs, and were carved all over with figures and faces, too many to count.

Although it was early in the morning, there were a good many people in the market. They had animals with them: cows, bulls, goats, and sheep. Everybody was talking. Their voices were not loud but friendly and musical.

Some shops where they were selling necklaces gave me the idea of buying one for Mother. I had no sooner begun to examine a necklace than the shopkeeper began telling me what wonderful silver it was, how it was carved by an artist, all handmade, and how there was nothing like it in all the world.

"Beautiful!" he kept saying right in my ear, while he smiled at me as if we had a secret together. "Beautiful! And cheap!" They all seemed to know enough English words to sell their stuff to tourists.

"How much is it?" I asked him.

"So cheap!" he exclaimed. "You will not believe! Only, I say, *only* sixteen rupees! You don't believe?"

Sixteen rupees. That was two dollars. It was certainly cheap.

I started to pull my wallet out, but Rama shoved my hand back into my pocket and fairly screeched at the old guy, "Robber! Thief! I am ashamed of you. Such a price for your worthless trash!"

I was bewildered.

"But—but it's only—" I began, but Rama's eyes flashed. He looked furious!

"This man is a villain!" he hissed in my ear, but so the old guy could hear him. "This necklace is inferior. It is bad silver. It is not worth one rupee! Two would be excessive!"

"He lies!" the old guy screamed. "This is silver that has no equal in all Nepal! It is worth twenty rupees!"

"Two rupees, robber!" Rama shouted.

"I make you a real bargain," the old man said to me, pretending Rama wasn't there. "Twelve rupees."

"Three at the most!" Rama said. "It is too much, but offer him three."

The merchant looked as if he were going to cry.

"You make a pauper of me!" he cried. "But I will give it to you for ten—no less. Otherwise my children starve."

"You lie, and your children grow fat over the profit you make from Americans," Rama yelled. "My friend will pay you five rupees. That is all, and no more bargaining. Out we go."

"Eight!" the man pleaded, so pitifully. "Eight! It is only because I wish to show that Nepal loves America. We give this bargain while my children are sick with hunger. Eight!"

"Eight it is," Rama said suddenly. "You are a robber, but my friend will give you eight rupees, and you will have a bad ending, and all your children will desert you in your old age." Then he turned to me. "Give the robber eight rupees!" he said.

Dizzily, I counted out the eight rupees, and the old man wrapped up the necklace in an unusual kind of paper, which Rama told me afterward was made from a cactus leaf. When that was done we were suddenly good friends. There wasn't another word about robbers. We went on our way with the old man shouting blessings after us.

I gasped then, and both Rama and Marty laughed.

"You see what I mean," Marty said. "That's bargaining!"

"But wasn't the necklace really worth more than—what I paid him?" I asked.

"It is a bargain," Rama agreed. "But half the first price asked is about right." And then he looked at his watch. "It is late. We must go at once to my home because my family will be waiting for us. We will ride cycle rickshas."

In Nepal the ricksha (they say, "cycle ricksha" or "pedisha") is like a bicycle, except that it has three wheels, one in front and two in back. Over the back wheels, or rather between them, is a little seat with a top like a buggy. Though it is big enough for two people, it is a tight fit. That's the passenger seat. The driver sits in front and pedals.

Of course, I'd been wanting to ride in one of those things ever since I first saw one the day before, and I had wondered if they were as jouncy as they looked. They were, but fun. Rama climbed in with me so he could tell me about things we passed, and Marty came behind in another one, with only the driver for company.

We couldn't go very fast through the crowded streets of the city, but that didn't bother me because there was plenty to see. At Marty's request, Rama told the driver to take us past a big pool right in the middle of town where they used to have trials.

"It was simple then," he said. "A man accused of a crime was thrown into the pool. If he was innocent, he did not sink. If guilty, he drowned."

"What kept him from drowning?" I asked.

Rama told me it was the support of the gods. I didn't comment, because I wasn't sure how seriously Rama took all this, but after a little pause he added, "That was before the revolution. We no longer use the pool for this purpose."

When we reached the quieter streets where there was less traffic, we really went spinning along. Those cyclists were strong men, and, as Rama said, we weren't such a heavy load, either.

Finally we came to the part of town where Rama lived. All the large houses there had walls surrounding their gardens, so we couldn't tell much about them.

I asked Rama why the gardens had walls, but he couldn't tell me. We stopped on a corner, walked about a block, and then went through a little gate into a garden. After that we went into the house, entering through a long dark hall. Before we entered the living room, we took off our shoes, a procedure that really surprised me. We never did that at the hotel, and nobody had happened to tell me it was a custom. We all went into the family living room.

It was beautiful in there—magnificent, really. There was a deep, silky, blue and gold and red Oriental carpet on the floor. All the furniture was heavy and carved. Most of it was little low tables and there were no chairs. I was so taken with the room at first that I didn't notice that the whole family was there to meet us.

Rama made the introductions in a most dignified way. First he presented us to his grandfather, then his mother and his aunt, and then his two sisters who were shy and giggly. Each one said, *"Namaste"* (which sounded like "na-mus-teh" and means either "hello" or "good-by"), and made the greeting gesture with hands together under the chin and the little bow. By that time I was beginning to feel that I knew how to give the Nepalese greeting.

As we were getting comfortable on the floor, two servants hustled around with various kinds of food: rice and vegetables and some kind of meat and tea in glasses (yes, glasses!). Milk and sugar were placed in the glasses before the tea was poured. I couldn't help wondering if it was buffalo milk. Rama's mother answered my unspoken question.

"I trust you use buffalo milk," she said. "We drink much of it in Nepal."

I told her I wasn't sure I'd ever tasted it but would certainly like to try.

Marty said he could not tell the difference between cow and buffalo milk. I found I couldn't either.

Three kinds of pastries were served. One was peppery with curry, another was sweet, and the third was a little like a doughnut, only heavier and greasier. I liked them all, but one of each was enough.

All during the meal I kept thinking how beautiful Rama's mother was. A good many of the people I saw in Katmandu were a mixture of Indian and Chinese, but the Prasads look pure Indian and very handsome. Mrs. Prasad seemed shy, but she spoke English and did most of the talking. The other two adults bowed and smiled, and the girls mostly giggled. One of them looked a little younger than Rama, but not much.

As the morning wore on, one of the sisters got brave and told us that her father might come to the United States next year. I asked if the rest of the family would come with him.

"No, no!" she exclaimed. "It is too much money!"

"Perhaps I shall come," Rama added. "Boys are favored in Nepal."

He laughed when he said it, but he was probably telling the truth. I hoped he would come, and meet my mother.

Mrs. Prasad asked me if I liked Nepal.

"I certainly do," I answered enthusiastically.

"What is best in Nepal?" she asked me.

I had to stop and think about that. "I like the people best," I said finally, "and after that the mountains."

That seemed to be just right. Everybody seemed delighted when Rama translated what I'd said.

"Dave wants to climb a mountain. He's read about Tensing Norkey and Sir Edmund Hillary climbing Everest," Marty told them.

That got them all excited, and they did a lot of talking back and forth in Nepali. They seemed to have a private joke among themselves.

Finally Rama said, "We were all talking about how much fun it would be for you both to go on a trek with my cousin, Neer, who is an expert climber. We'd like you both to meet Neer. Will you excuse me please? I will be only a minute."

Things seemed to move fast then, but Marty seemed to be taking it all calmly. Rama was back in a minute. With him came one of the handsomest, outdoorsy-looking guys I ever saw. A real mountain climber!

But that wasn't the most amazing thing that happened. Not near! After the introductions and bowings, Rama explained to his cousin (at least, I guess he did—he spoke in Nepali) that we wanted to go on a trek. Neer looked at me and repeated my name. Then he asked some more questions and clapped his hands together. When he talked to Rama, I could see he was saying something startling. Rama looked as if he couldn't believe his ears.

"This is too strange," he exclaimed in English, "but it is true!"

"What's true?" Marty demanded. "Why don't you let Dave and me in on all this?"

"But it is amazing!" Rama repeated. "You see, my cousin will go on a trek next week to Ama Kmu in the Gurkha country. That is where the United Mission Community Center is located. The journey is being arranged especially with the hope that David Conklin Brown will be able to go. It is *for* you! Only no one has had an opportunity to speak to your father about it."

Well, I guess I nearly fell over at that news. All I could say was that I hoped Marty could go, too. Neer said, "But of course! It will be an easy trek, made especially for Americans!"

That wasn't too flattering, but it didn't offend Marty.

"Next week!" I exclaimed.

"To the Gurkha country!" Marty added.

I didn't show my appreciation as well as I should have, but they all seemed to understand and were excited, too. Rama said of course he would go with us. In fact, everything seemed to be settled right then, except that nobody had said anything to Dad.

By that time it was nearly noon, and I was wondering how to get away from a party like this one where people were so hospitable that it seemed almost insulting to leave. Somehow we did it, and the whole group saw us to the door. We said *namaste* over and over again, and Rama's sisters and the rest of them all waved. You'd have thought though we were already starting on that trek! (It seems as if that's the way they do things in Nepal. Everything is an occasion.)

Rama went with us down the street to where we got a little jeep bus. He gave directions to the driver about where we wanted to get off. The bus started with a jerk, and as soon as we were on our way I settled back and said, "Well!" and Marty said, "What did I tell you? Aren't they swell? And what do you think about that trek they've gotten ready for us—for you, I mean."

"You, too," I said. "Will your folks let you go?"

"Oh sure, they'll be glad to have me off their hands for a couple of weeks," Marty said. "My folks believe kids should be independent and live their own lives." It sounded good, but I wasn't quite convinced. Then he added, "How about your Dad?"

"I think he believes in independence, too," I said. "But I don't know how much. He'll probably go along with this idea, though, because Mr. Kingston planned it. He's the missionary in charge of Ama Kmu. It really was swell of him, wasn't it?"

We didn't say anything for a while, because we were both thinking. Finally I said the only thing that bothered me was that this trek wouldn't take us to Everest, the mountain I wanted to go to.

"Everest?" Marty sounded as if nothing could be less important. "Who wants to go there?" He turned up his nose a little. "Why, Everest is getting to be old hat—*everybody* goes there! It's practically a four-lane superhighway for tourists. Gurkha country is a lot more exciting. And we'll go toward Annapurna—ever hear of that?"

Had I ever heard of Annapurna? *Had* I! I let out a whoop that made the driver turn around and grin at us.

"Gee-oh!" I shouted, "Annapurna!"

5. *Toward the Eternal Snows*

IF I LIVE TO BE TWO HUNDRED, I'LL ALWAYS REMEMBER THAT first night in the Himalayas. The other fellows on the trek, especially our Nepalese porters, probably thought it was crazy. Or maybe they just thought it was an old American custom to write in a notebook by flashlight!

Here is what I wrote:

"We are close to the stars tonight! The fire is out on which we cooked our supper a while ago. Everybody else is rolled up in his sleeping bag and tucked 'way under the wide ledge of rock behind the fire site. It's so cold out here that my fingers are almost too stiff to hold a pencil, but cold or not, this night has got to go down in the record.

"Some place in the distance there's a faint far-off noise like an animal moaning, which could be the Abominable Snowman himself, for all I know! *Yeti,* they call him. Everything else is quiet tonight in the High Himalayas.

"And what stars! Big as bushel baskets, so bright it hurts to look at them, and you feel mighty close to something that's bigger than stars. You, yourself—you're *so small!*

"It seems as though a place like this, at a time like this, makes it necessary to think about things you don't think about much and hardly ever talk about.

"We're Hindus, a Jew, and a Christian bedded down here together, and God is a greater mystery than ever before in my life. The more you see, the less you can understand—and the more you have to believe. There couldn't be an atheist, I guess, in the High Himalayas at night!"

But I'm getting ahead of my story.

When I got back and told Dad about the party at the Prasads', he congratulated me on getting around so well in Katmandu. He'd already heard from Mr. Kingston about the expedition, so that wasn't a surprise, but just as I had expected, he wasn't quite sure about it. However, Mr. Kingston's message had about convinced him. If Dad could have made the trip himself, of course, he wouldn't have hesitated a minute. But he had to make one of those quicky trip down to India and then up to Pakistan that very week.

"I wish we could talk to your mother about this," he said to me.

"But we know exactly what she'd say," I protested. "She'd say it was a crazy idea and foolish and dangerous. And then she'd say, of *course* to go and to be careful. And then she'd say to bring back a blow-by-blow report about the Community Center for her to use in a missionary program!"

Dad chuckled at that. Then he nodded seriously. "She'd be right, too!" he said. "You've sold me, Dave. You must go, and you must be careful. But this is the opportunity of your life to see one of the most interesting and worthwhile pieces of missionary work that the church is doing anywhere. I only wish I could go with you."

"What about Shanta Bhawan?" I asked, remembering the column that I was supposed to do for Dad.

"After you get back," he said, "Shanta Bhawan will be waiting for you!"

As for Marty, well, he was right about his folks. The Rosens thought it was an excellent idea, because they always encouraged Martin to live his own life. After Dad got a chance to talk to Rama's father and met Rama's cousin, who came over to the hotel to look at the maps with him, he felt pretty sure it was all right.

Of course, there was a terrific amount of getting ready to do. In some ways it was worse than packing to go to Nepal, because, of all the things in the world I wasn't prepared for, the biggest was to make a hiking trip through the snow-capped mountains of Asia. We really had to start from scratch with equipment. But trust Mr. Kingston! He'd sent instructions about what we'd need to buy: thick-soled shoes, a sleeping bag, blankets, a canteen, a lantern, a flashlight, and most important of all, a good reliable walking stick. He said that would be a third leg, and everybody climbing the mountains needed all the legs he could get. There were other things, including tinned food, but those were the most important. Neer and the porters took care of most of the food supplies.

Then there were some instructions to memorize about safe conduct. As we followed the trail, we were to stick together, and there was a way of signaling if we got lost. We weren't supposed to drink water from the streams or even the springs without asking Neer. Always we were to wait for his instructions about crossing bridges and fording streams, and even about taking trails. He knew the way!

And finally we had a map that Mr. Kingston sent us, showing exactly the route we'd take. I made two copies, one for Rama and one for Marty, and kept the original for myself. It was going to take us six days to get to the Community Center over a northerly route, and seven days to get back on a southerly route. I admired the way the mountains were drawn on that little map—rows and curly rows of rippling peaks. If you want to see the route we were to take, turn to pages 72 and 73.

Planning a trek, especially for tenderfeet like Marty and me, is a full-time job of several days. But at last we were as ready as we ever would be, as Marty said. We were to leave the hotel before dawn. Early as it was, Marty's mother and father were up earlier, and my dad was with them to see us off. We had a small send-off at the hotel, too, with two or three porters and attendants out in front telling us good-by. When we were finally piled into the jeep, with our sleeping bags and stuff around us, we began to feel our trek was a real expedition—Arctic or South Pole, not to mention the Himalayas!

It was just daybreak when the jeep stopped on the far side of town, fairly close to where our trail started up the mountain. The others were there already. Besides Rama and Neer, who was the leader, there were four porters. Two of the porters were twins, Rama told me, and that's considered very good luck. Their names were Bir, which means "courageous," and Buddhi Bir, which is Nepali for "brave and clever." They looked exactly alike.

In fact, all four of the porters looked alike to me. They were of Tibetan ancestry, Rama told us; Sherpas, they are called in Nepal.

I knew about the Sherpas because of Tensing Norkey, but these men were the first I'd met, and it was a surprise to see how small they were and how large the packs were that they carried. Each porter carried seventy pounds.

"Of course, they are very strong," Rama said of the Sherpa porters. "Strength is not in size."

It reminded me of Tensing again, and how Sherpa boys don't consider a load a burden, but a pleasure, and part of the fun! Those Sherpas are wonderful people!

We thought maybe it was a good omen that just as we got our last straps adjusted, and were ready to take off up the mountain, the sun began to fill the sky. Our way was to be up toward the top of the rim that had looked like the side of a deep pan or plate when I saw it from the plane. Marty and I soon learned that experienced climbers had a rhythm to their walking that made it easier. I concentrated on keeping the pace and trying to get that rhythm. Rama and the others talked mostly in Nepali and mostly about us I gathered, because they repeated "American" often. They probably wondered whether the Americans could make the trek!

The trail began to get steeper fast, which made the walking seem faster, too, but even so I had no idea how we were progressing until suddenly Neer gave a shout. We all stopped dead in our tracks, looked around, and only then realized that we were on top of the first high ridge that made the rim of the Katmandu bowl. Looking back over the way we'd come, we could see Katmandu sparkling and glittering below us.

But looking the other way, the direction in which we were going, we saw a tossing ocean of clouds, which shifted and changed to show glimpses and then whole distant views of mountains and deep valleys, as far as our eyes could see. Our route was among the clouds!

As soon as the Sherpas saw that I was interested in getting acquainted with them, they went all out to be friendly. We all taught one another a few words of our different lan-

guages while we were having our rests along the way, and it was surprising how quickly I learned a few useful words of Nepali. I already knew *namaste,* "hello" and "good-by," and I found *danyabad,* "thank you," very useful, too.

After the first rest stop on the rim, we tightened our straps and started into the "beyond." Neer strode along in front, looking like a giant among us short people. He was the tallest Oriental I ever saw, easily six feet. Although his steps were long, his gait was steady. Neer sure knew how to lead!

As it opened, the way consisted of long steep descents down the mountain to a river or stream at the bottom, crossing the water, and then maybe a long walk along the riverbank for some miles. Then we'd begin climbing up another mountain and possibly walking along the ridge for a while before we plunged down into the next valley to cross another river or stream.

At first it was hard, but then I began to catch my second wind. Marty said afterwards that the same thing happened to him. We walked sometimes for fifteen, sometimes thirty minutes at a stretch, depending upon the porters. They were the ones with the heavy loads and were the pace setters. We had to keep up with them. When they called a long halt for a hot meal, I was so in the habit of putting one foot ahead of the other that it was hard to stop. First thing we'd do would be to drop our packs on the ground and relax. Then one of the porters would either gather wood and build a fire or get out a little alcohol stove. We always had a fire at night, though, because it was cold.

We ate two hot meals a day, one at midmorning and the other at night. In between we nibbled on snacks of cookies, nuts, candy, or fruit that we'd buy in the villages along the way. Our hot meal always consisted of very generous portions of boiled rice and two side dishes that we mixed with the rice to help it down. One of the side dishes was called *dahl* and was a sort of a thick split-pea soup. The other side dish was either a meat or vegetable mixture.

One big memory that stands out about our first afternoon in the mountains was the first footlog. I'd seen plenty of footlogs before, of course. There are some scary ones over the ravines in the mountains where Mom and Dad and I had camped. This first footlog in the Himalayas, though, was the grandfather of them all. It had no grooves, and it was worn smooth, even slick in places. But the worst thing was that that log connected the two banks of one of the fastest streams I can remember. It probably wasn't half as bad as it looked, and Rama insisted it was only ten feet wide, but it looked like a boiling cauldron to me. I began to tremble at the thought of having to cross it with nothing to hold on to. We approached it from rather a wide bit of trail, so I saw it coming and watched the men, beginning with Neer, go across as if it were a sidewalk. Marty was ahead of me, and when he got to it he stopped. I understood. I stopped, too, and Rama, who was behind me, had to stop, and so did Bir at the end.

Neer noticed that we were behind, and beckoned us to come on. "Don't look down," he called. "Look at the leader!" Neer reached out a hand from the other side to Marty, who looked at me and went across. My turn next. My heart was going double quick! Marty had done it, so I couldn't look like a tenderfoot. I gritted my teeth, looked at Neer's outstretched hand—miles away!—and went! It was all I could do to keep from looking down at the water below.

ROUTE OF THE EXPEDITION

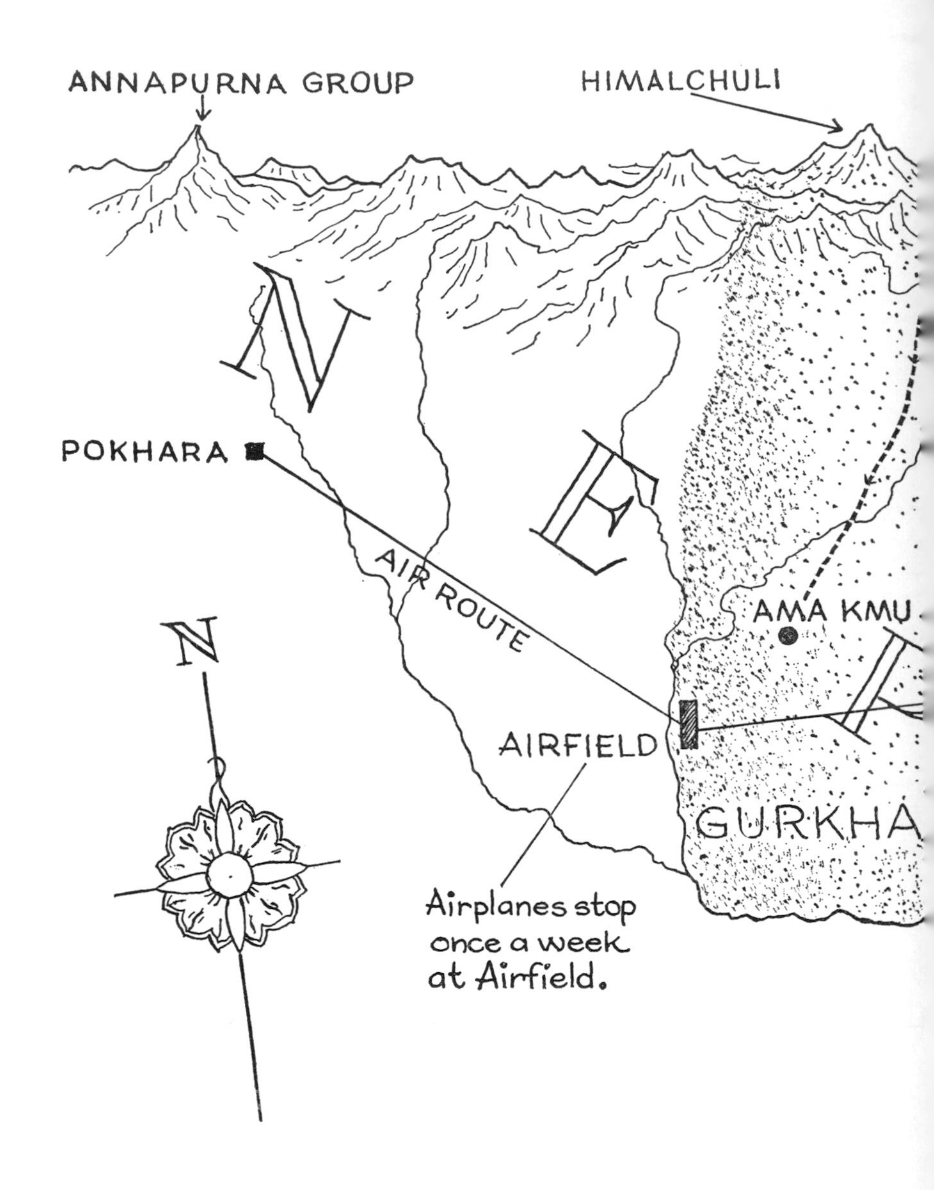

ROM KATMANDU TO AMA KMU

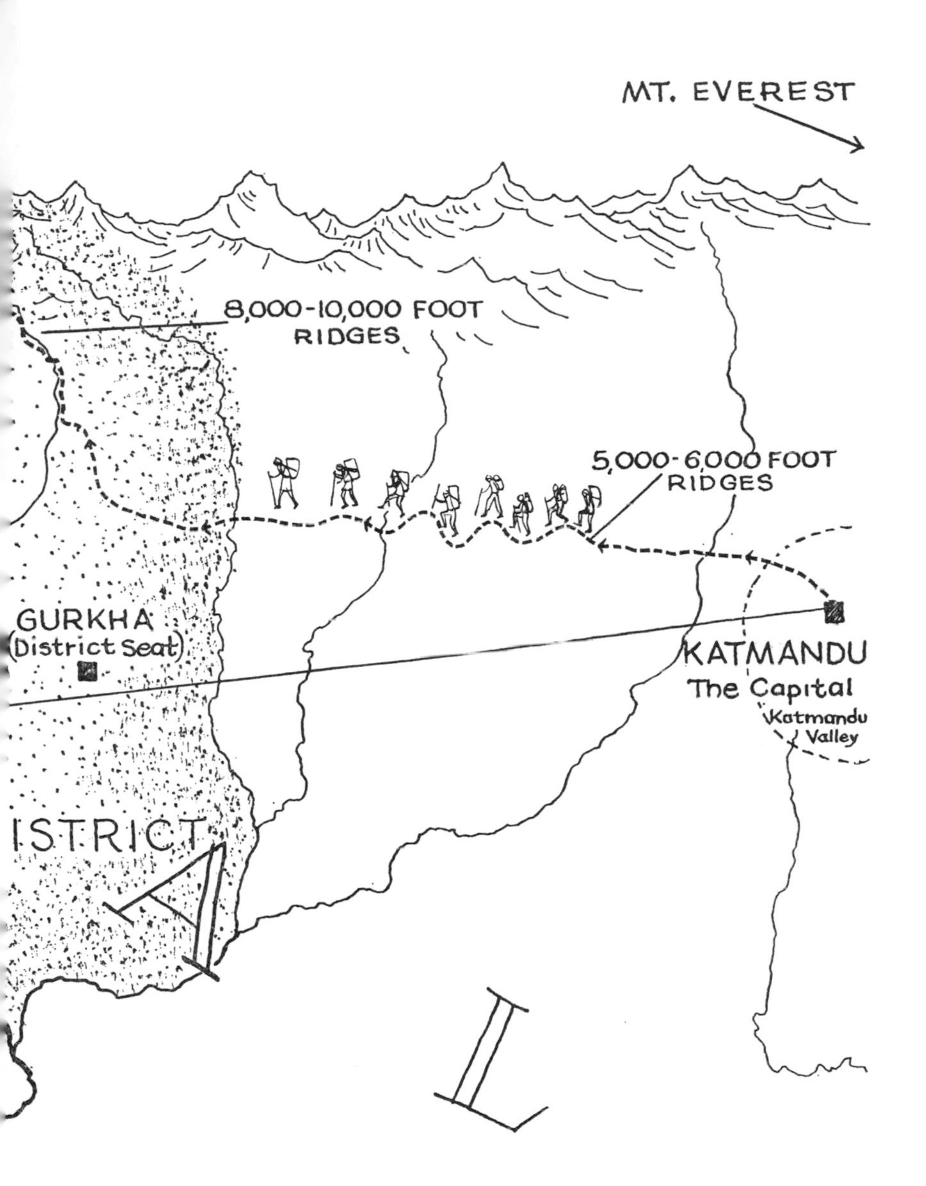

Once on the other side, I felt like fainting, except that I knew that would have been as bad as slipping on the log, or not going across at all. Marty looked as white as a sheet, and I must have, too. He grinned at me and said, "We made it, Dave!"

And that was that. It was only the first log, however, for we met others every day. By the time we finally stopped earlier tonight, I had done and seen just about as much as I could take! I ached all over, especially the muscles I never knew I had.

The men made a fire, and we all gathered pieces of wood from nearby. After we'd eaten, everybody gathered around the fire to talk. Except that the conversation was in Nepali, which Rama interpreted to us North Americans, it could have been a campfire in the Canadian Rockies or any place. Maybe campfires make people all over the world remember stories and tell them.

After a while I asked about the Abominable Snowman. Rama translated my question for the porters. They laughed, but they were serious, too, and I thought they looked a little scared.

"Yeti!" they kept saying. *"Yeti!"*

"Yeti is the Nepalese name for this creature," Neer said. "No one has ever seen him, only his tracks. Perhaps *Yeti* is an animal. These men believe *Yeti* must be a spirit that can vanish at once."

"But how does a spirit make tracks?" I asked.

"I do not know," Rama answered. "No one knows."

"Any man who sees *Yeti* must die," Neer added. "Therefore no one living has seen it. But we can hear. We will no doubt hear *Yeti* tonight when the fire is low. . . ."

Was it real, or did we just imagine that we heard the sound of scratching in the woods after our voices had grown quiet and the fire was nearly out? Later, after all the others had gotten into their sleeping bags, I sat outside my tent for a little while and wrote that page in my journal. Then at last I snuggled down into my sleeping bag.

"Yeti!" I could hear the men mutter, half in fun, half in fear. *"Yeti!"*

6. *Second Day on Trek*

SOMETHING, I DON'T KNOW WHAT, WAKENED ME EARLY THE next morning while everything was still dark. Maybe an animal was sniffing around, or maybe it was *Yeti*. Of course, it could have been somebody snoring in another tent. Anyway, I began remembering the stories Neer and Bir had told the night before, and how we'd heard, or thought we'd heard, that moaning and scratching out in the woods.

It was too cold, though, to get out of the sleeping bag, and pretty soon the sniffing stopped. After that everything was quiet. I lay there and, through a small hole in the tent wall, watched the dawn begin to light the sky. It was just as wonderful as watching the daylight turn into evening. Little by little the big sky began getting a pale gingeraley color, until you could see sunlight glittering on the snowy peaks. It was like beginning all over, or like starting to write on a new page.

I noticed that Rama was beginning to stir, and I wondered if he'd been wakened by that sniffing, too. I couldn't stay in bed any longer, so I got up and went outside. Upon a ledge about twenty feet above our camp was Neer, standing like a statue outlined against the sky. He looked as if he might be praying. I wondered if Hindus greeted the dawn with prayer.

Looking down in the direction he was facing, I could see the deep ravine through which the river cut and the path that ran alongside it. It was the very path we had traveled the day before. Neer's glance turned then, and mine turned with his to look up and along our trail, climbing higher and finally disappearing around a bend far above our camp. It looked as though that must be our next route.

"What's he doing up there?" Marty whispered. I was surprised to see that he was up, too!

"He looks at the weather," answered Rama, who had also gotten up. "He looks at the distance we have come and the direction we will go."

That sounded like praying, too, in a way.

Suddenly everybody was sitting up and rolling out. Things happened fast after that.

Breakfast was a cup of tea and what Rama called a biscuit. We would call it a cracker at home. Rama said this was to fortify us for the early morning part of the day's trek. If I had known what was coming in the next little while, I probably would have had another one of those biscuits.

It was the footlogs that fooled me. We met two or three rather quickly, because the stream we had crossed the day before began doubling back. Or perhaps our trail doubled back to meet the stream. Anyway, I had learned, or thought I had, how to keep my balance on a log and to throw my weight in the opposite direction when it began to roll too far over the wrong way. It seemed to be quite a trick, although Neer and the rest were not especially impressed by my skill.

Altogether, I was getting pretty brave and was beginning to feel like an old hand. Once I even turned around to see if Rama had noticed what a good job I was doing. That was my undoing. It was exactly then that my foot slipped.

I did a neat flip-flop and dived right straight for the water. I yelled, but my loudest noise was a mighty splash that sounded like an explosion.

The water wasn't deep, and the log wasn't high, so there was nothing dangerous about it, which was a real piece of good luck. Neer was after me almost faster than I fell in. He dragged me out, pack and all, before I had a chance to be scared or anything.

Except for a bump on my knee, the only thing that really got hurt was my pride. Rama tried to smooth that over by telling me it happened all the time. "Even the experienced ones slip on the logs," he said. "My cousin Neer sometimes falls!"

I looked at Neer, and he grinned back at me. I'd have bet anything he hadn't fallen off a footlog in a long, long time! But it was nice of Rama to say that, and Marty tried to help out, too.

"It's just plain luck I didn't go in myself," he declared. "There's no way in the world to tell how slick a log is going to be." Then he added, "Of course, I've got it figured out scientifically, and I can tell you how to do it if you want me to."

"I had it figured out scientifically, too," I told him. "It didn't work."

"The footlogs are not bad," Rama interrupted. "They are, what you might say, the beginning of the difficulties."

"What's the end then?" I asked, feeling my knee as we went along.

Rama laughed and told us to watch out for cable bridges. I secretly hoped Marty would be the one to fall off one of those. But when, about a hundred yards farther on, we went around a bend and walked plump into the first swinging bridge of the trek, I certainly didn't hope Marty or anybody would fall off it.

There is nothing you can compare a swinging bridge with. It's a sort of sidewalk, but narrower than an ordinary sidewalk and made of boards strung along together with heavy cables. The boards make a long wooden ribbon, and the cables anchor it on either end to trees or big posts or rocks. I learned later that the cables had been carried all this distance by men on foot maybe as long as sixty years ago. The cables had come from Scotland, of all places, and were good and stout, thick as a man's wrist. There was no danger of the cables breaking, to my mind. Rama said they did break sometimes, however. What bothered me was the swinging, and over such a deep chasm!

Swinging is exactly the word, too. There's usually a wind, often quite a strong one, blowing across these canyons, so a bridge is apt to be in gentle motion to start with. Then when a lot of people begin going across, it jiggles and shakes up and down and sways back and forth all at the same time. Most bridges have railings on each side, but even railings don't make you feel completely safe when you're dipping and jumping along in the middle, with nothing between you and the rocks below except fifty or sixty feet of fresh air!

Neer and two of the porters went first, of course. It was no problem for them. Marty was supposed to go next, but he stopped to think it over.

"Carry on," I told him. "You're holding up the procession."

"How about you doing it?" he asked. "This'll make a better tumble than that footlog—something to write home about!"

That made me mad and courageous.

"I don't want to steal the whole show," I said. "You can have the honor of this ducking. But I'll carry on so as to leave you plenty of room!"

With that I stomped onto the little bridge, barely hearing Neer shout after me, "Look to the farther mountain! Do not look down!"

I was too mad to know exactly how it all felt, but I careened across somehow, and stumbled over the last board onto good solid earth on the other side.

Marty cheered as he started along behind, and we shook hands when he swayingly made it across. I certainly didn't wish for him to fall off, but it would have helped if he'd stubbed his toe at the end, or done some small thing like that. We had to admit it wasn't bad, and when you analyzed it, it certainly was not as difficult as those slippery foot-logs.

By this time Rama had already strolled across as easily as if he'd been walking on a sidewalk in New York. He said hardly anyone ever falls off a cable bridge. The danger is all in the imagination, he assured us.

As we started hiking along the trail again, Marty and I joked about what the next "difficulty" would be. He hoped it would be the real-life *Yeti*.

Later that afternoon we met the "difficulty." It was not *Yeti,* it was worse. It was another river to cross, much wider and with more rapids, but this time—not even a foot-log. There had been one, we could see, but it had washed away, probably in a flood. And there we were. The porters and Neer and Rama all had a conference while Marty and I stood by, wondering what they were planning. We soon found out.

Neer announced, "We will have to ford this river. The

current is too swift for a single person. We go two and three abreast."

"Swimming?" I asked doubtfully.

"Not swimming, wading," Rama said. "The water is too swift and besides you've got a pack to carry. You must move across faster than the current!"

Marty and I looked at each other. It didn't make much sense, and it sure sounded difficult.

Three of the porters demonstrated. They formed a human chain, holding hands, rushing into the rapids up to their waists. They seemed to meet the current at a sort of angle. It was amazing. We whistled.

"That is a beautiful sight!" Marty said. "But it appears I'm not the outdoor boy I thought I was. Aren't there rocks in the water? How did they keep from slipping on them?"

"You can slip," Rama admitted. "But it is easier to be barefoot. You will take off the shoes." We did and tied them onto our packs.

Then Rama looked at me, and I couldn't pretend not to see.

"O.K.," I said. "The sooner I start, the sooner it will be over. Who's going to be on my team?"

It appeared they weren't taking any chances with me. I had the best. Neer took hold of one of my hands and Bir the other.

"Now you will hold each hand tightly," Rama warned.

"We go forward, together as one person," Neer instructed, "a little bit with the river."

I saw what he meant. You made it as easy as you could by staying with the current and not trying to buck it.

"And on the rocks—they are slippery—step lightly!" he said.

We joined hands, and I hung on as instructed. The current was so strong and pulled so hard that I felt like a cork. I could feel my feet slipping on the rocks on the bottom. I was sure I was going to fall, but the other two dragged me along. Before I had time to be scared, we were climbing up on the other side, soaked to the skin. And was I out of breath!

I had a moment of satisfaction when they all cheered on both sides of the river. And I had another mean kind of moment when it was Marty's turn and he went down! Rama and Buddhi Bir yanked him up again right away, so there was no harm, only a lot of sputtering. It sure was funny though.

"Graceful as a hippopotamus!" I remarked for fun, but then I saw it wasn't fun for Marty.

"Why, kid, you really did a thing, pulling yourself up in those rapids!" I said quickly. "It was nice going, wasn't it, Rama?"

"It was very nice going!" Rama repeated at once.

Marty tried to look a little happier. I could see it hurt him to look foolish, but he was game.

"How soon do we try the next ford?" he asked. "I want to try that stunt again quick before I forget the technique. That's really quite a stunt!"

Then he looked at me quizzically. "I guess we're tied now, Dave," he said. "It's your turn to pull a bloomer next, boy! Make it good!"

"It'll be good!" I said laughing. "I haven't quite made up my mind what, but it'll be good."

When it finally happened, it was very good!

7. *Green Salad*

MY FAMOUS ESCAPADE WAITED FOR THE SIXTH DAY OUT, WHEN we were almost at the end of our trek. In a way it was Marty's fault, although he never would admit it. It was all because he didn't like rice.

We had both been getting steadily more fed up with the rations, although Rama told us lots of Nepalese live all their lives on mostly rice and *dahl*. By the sixth day Marty had stopped fussing, but he had begun doing something worse. He was reciting long lists of things he liked to eat, like steak and ice cream and fresh green salad.

"If I could just have a mouthful of good green salad, I

guess I could die happy," he was moaning that very morning, while we were washing down our biscuits with hot tea.

"For breakfast?" I asked. "Who ever heard of green salad for breakfast?"

"No, for lunch or brunch or whatever you call it," he said. "I want to look forward to something besides the *same!*"

"Nothing's stopping you from looking forward," I said sarcastically, because I was getting kind of tired of the way he kept complaining about the food.

But when Marty said "green salad," Rama's eyes began to shine. "I will show you a green salad," he said. "You can gather it all around here, and you can cook it, too, if you wish."

Rama's "green salad" was a leaf that grew on a tree there. It looked like spinach, and it was ruffled. It was practically tasteless, maybe even a little bitter. Rama said it was better cooked and chopped. Marty didn't care how it was served, just so long as it was green.

"Green is the prettiest color there is," he declared, "especially for eating!"

Rama showed us the leaves and from that time on we three pulled off leaves whenever we saw one of those trees. But we kept up with the trek. When lunch time came it was sort of exciting with all those weeds we'd been collecting. Marty and Rama and I pooled all we had and then scattered out to look for some more.

My idea, as I remember now, was to poke around the edges of the level place where we had stopped to eat. But the "green salad" kept luring me on a little farther and a little farther, until finally I was far out of sight of the camp and probably out of earshot, too.

At last I saw a really big bunch growing on a tree out on the edge of a narrow kind of low ledge. The branch with the best leaves leaned way out over the edge. I thought my stick would be in the way so I laid it down. I jumped down onto the ledge and began edging my way out toward the tree, grabbing at bushes to keep from falling. Finally I got to the tree. Holding on to the trunk with one hand, I reached out as far as I could with the other hand after a bunch of leaves.

That was when I heard a little noise behind me—like pebbles falling. I froze! Then goose pimples began to rise all over my body. My first thought was of a landslide. I *had* to see what was happening behind me, I just had to! But my neck muscles would not let my head turn to look.

All this couldn't have taken more than a half a second, but it seemed like an hour while I slowly, slowly got my head to twist around—and—then I saw it!

It was a bear, smiling right into my eyes, about a foot and a half away. I'll never forget it!

We stayed there, the bear and I, for maybe two seconds, although it seemed more like an hour. Maybe we were both scared. I had the advantage, though, because at least I knew he was a bear. All I could think of was, why, he's not so

very big. He's not much bigger than a good-sized dog. And look at him smile!

Suddenly everything unfroze.

I tried to get to my feet, but all of a sudden the ledge gave way under me. For a second I was swinging out in space, still holding on to the tree. Then the whole tree was uprooted away from the cliff.

I can remember wondering somewhere on the way down why everything was so quiet, and why nobody screamed. That was all!

Sometimes, looking back, I think to myself that if I'd screamed or yelled, they might have heard me back at camp. On the other hand, a yell might have made the bear decide to go after me, and then—

But as Marty says, I didn't, they didn't, and the bear didn't.

If the Gurkha boy hadn't come along right soon—

But that's the next chapter.

8. *Gurkha Hospitality*

I'LL NEVER KNOW WHAT FINALLY HIT ME OR WHAT I HIT, because the next thing I knew, I was coming to with a pain thumping like crazy in the back of my head, just as if somebody were hitting me with a hammer. I wanted to scream at the thumping to stop, but all that came out was a sort of moan, and even that hurt. But it may have been the moan that finally pulled me out of my coma, for I seemed to come back, back, back, even though it hurt. My eyes opened little by little, as if a door were slowly opening on its hinges.

I seemed to be lying on a hard floor. There were some

people around, how many I couldn't tell, but one seemed to be a boy. Anyway, he was wearing the kind of Gurkha knife Mr. Kingston had drawn back in Chicago. Gradually the crowd of faces got sorted out so that I could see a man, then a woman, and then some other kid, and some animals.

As I got used to the darkness of the place, I could tell we were in a room with a mud floor. I found out later the walls were mud also. There was a woven straw mat under me. It was like a carpet, except that it was really a bed, Nepalese style. There didn't seem to be much furniture, yet the room seemed full, with clothes hanging on the wall, blankets rolled up and stacked in a corner, a little smoky fire right in the middle of the floor, and big bins that looked like square baskets, woven of some kind of stalks that looked like bamboo. The bins were around the wall, and I was told later that they were full of rice.

Nobody talked; but as soon as they saw I was conscious, the woman got up and brought me a little cup or bowl of something that smelled like spoiled juice. (Rama told me later that it was millet beer and is called *chang*.) The woman set the bowl down on the floor beside me, with both hands, made a bow, and then sat down on the floor again. But she didn't exactly sit. Nepalese have a way of squatting, for hours at a time. It's almost as if they sit on a low stool, except that there isn't any stool!

The first whiff of that sour stuff was bad enough, but the second made me feel like being sick. Right then my eyes cooperated by closing again.

While I lay there wondering vaguely where I was and what had happened, the people sitting around began to talk. It was soft and musical. They were certainly talking about me. Although the words were strange, the tone sounded familiar. I knew somehow that there was no need to be afraid.

I didn't know one thing about these people, except that since this was Nepal, they must be Nepalese, and since we were in Gurkha country, they were probably Gurkhas. Rama had told us the Gurkhas were warriors. Back here in the mountains, they wouldn't know much about Westerners. Who could tell if they would be friends or enemies of a foreign person? But I wasn't afraid!

I kept trying to think of what it was their talk reminded me of. There was something about the house, the people, and the way they talked that rang a bell back in my memory. I began to wonder if I'd known them in another life. I'd heard Hindus believe you keep coming back.

With my eyes still shut, I thought of how it all might have happened. In between the thumping in my head, it came to me that I must have fallen somewhere near a village. Or perhaps our party had been near a village when we stopped to fix our lunch. I remembered going off to look for "green salad." And I remembered the tree and the bear. But when had that happened? How long ago had it been?

Someone from this hut must have discovered me down in the canyon. It might even have been the boy, since he was sitting closest to me and watching me carefully. I wondered, too, but not so much, about our trek. It wasn't pleasant to think of how mad Neer must be to have the whole expedition upset. At that point thinking got harder, and my head hurt worse than ever.

When I finally opened my eyes again, maybe quite a while later, the people and the animals were still there. The only one who was not there was the boy with the kukri. He was gone, and in his place there was a girl. Her long black hair shone in the light that came through somewhere. She was pretty, with big dark eyes.

Once again the woman came to me with a bowl of something. Everything seemed clearer now, and I could see that the bowl was brass. Like the little girl's, the woman's face looked kind. She had a ring in her nose, too, but by this time it didn't look odd at all. The bowl of stuff smelled like tea. It was good and hot, fresh off the fire, which was making the whole room smoky and a little too warm. The woman held the tea close to my lips to make it easier for me to drink. The tea had milk and sugar in it, all right—probably the milk was buffalo! When I raised myself up to try to drink, I realized that my head was not the only part of me that had gotten bumped. A pain shot through my shoulder as if somebody had stuck a knife right in the blade. Maybe I yelled. Anyway, I fell back on the floor and waited for the pain to go away. Slowly, slowly, it finally did.

Of course, while all this was happening, time was going

by, too. There was no way of knowing how much time had already passed or what time of day it was now.

Suddenly in the midst of the state of semiconsciousness I seemed to be floating in, there were voices, familiar voices, coming from outside the house. The thumping in my head may have kept me from recognizing them right away, because it wasn't until there was a loud whisper in English that I began to get my bearings.

"Is Dave *dead?*" I heard Marty whisper.

Maybe it was the idea of being *dead* that brought me to life in a special hurry! I opened both eyes, tried to sit up, and yelled, "Ouch." Then there was a lot of moving around, and more people seemed to be coming in, like great shadows.

"Gee, Dave, you must be alive after all!" Marty said out loud, and Rama said something in Nepali. Perhaps he was too excited to remember his English.

I began to get better fast after that, although my arm hurt with the least little move. First of all, Rama told me that we were in a Gurkha hut. Next I wanted to know what time it was but discovered my watch was broken. It said 11:15, the time of my tumble, apparently.

"It is now late afternoon," Rama said. "This boy has led us here." He indicated the boy with the kukri who was again squatting in his place by the bed.

Rama told me the boy had been the one who found me. After I was brought back to the hut, he set out to find our party and guide them back to the hut.

As usual Marty had plenty to say. "Dave, you really broke up the party!" he exclaimed. "You disappeared. You know you shouldn't have left the others the way you did. Neer nearly had a fit. You ought to have seen the way he put Rama and me in the custody of good old Buddhi Bir. He told Rama and me that if either of us moved from the place, he'd do something fierce. Then Neer and the rest of our group scattered around to try to find you. You really created quite a commotion, Dave!"

He stopped for breath, while Rama went on telling the story. "My cousin was in distress!" he said. "They could not find you. But at last this Gurkha boy discovered the place where our fire was smoking. He came and reported that a Westerner had been found unconscious down in a canyon. So here we are."

While Rama and Marty talked to me, Neer was outside talking to the man of the family. Neer called to Rama, who rushed outside and just as quickly returned.

"They wish for you to stay in the house overnight," Rama said, "but my cousin says you must go to the clinic quickly, because your arm is injured. He says we will travel tonight to Ama Kmu."

"It may be kind of slow for you," I said.

"You are not to walk," Rama explained. "You will have to ride."

I tried to stand up to prove I could walk, but it was hard to move without hurting my arm. Neer made a neat sling out of tree bark and a kind of heavy scarf the woman gave him. It seemed there wasn't much that Neer couldn't do! Although I had to admit finally that it would be silly for me to try to walk, it wasn't clear how in the world they'd manage to carry me.

"What about the blankets?" I asked.

Neer laughed and said, "We will give all the blankets to this lazy Martin to carry!" Neer and Marty both laughed, and Marty said he thought he'd try to find a bear. (My bear story had really made a hit!)

Neer said that if Marty got chased by a bear, the party would be glad to leave him behind to take care of himself, and Rama said he'd feel sorry for the bear. All this went back and forth in both languages, and the Gurkha folks about laughed their heads off. They really enjoyed a joke. In fact, all the Nepalese I saw seemed like real happy people.

They had millet beer all around, except for Marty and me. He couldn't take the sour stuff either. We both liked the curry taste of the gravy they put on the rice, though, and I liked the little brass tea bowls, too. They gave me two for souvenirs. Marty had warned me to be careful about admiring anything a Nepalese was wearing or using, because he'd be sure to take it off and give it to you. But, as Marty says, we Westerners just keep doing the wrong things, and the Nepalese just keep on being polite!

More and more I kept trying to figure out what all this reminded me of. It was like being haunted!

Well, I had been wondering all the time about how they

were going to carry me, and Rama kept telling me to wait, there was no problem. Finally he said, "Now you will see."

Then I saw what he meant. Two men came through the door with my "stretcher." It was like a big basket, woven of bamboo and tipped so I could sit in it and swing my legs

over the side. After they had fastened me in the basket, they hoisted it up on Buddhi Bir's shoulders and we were ready to go. I managed to hold my bad arm with my good one, so it didn't jounce much when we moved. It hurt, but not too much.

When it was finally time to say good-by to the Gurkhas, I said *danyabad,* "thank you," over and over.

When we started off, the woman brought me the brass bowls, and the man gave me a kukri. Of course, I'd been dying to have one, but I didn't remember saying so out loud! He must have read my mind. Rama said it is the custom for Nepalese to give gifts. So I said, "Please tell them that they have already given me the best gift, which is life. Tell them I know they saved mine."

Rama said that in Nepali, and they all bowed.

"Tell them I will never forget them, and will consider that the Gurkha boy is my brother," I said.

He told them that, and the boy said something. When Rama interpreted to me, his words meant, "When you come again to Nepal, our home is your home. You are not a stranger."

We all said *namaste,* "good-by," and I repeated *danyabad* for as long as they could hear me. Riding along on Buddhi Bir's strong shoulders, I watched them until they were out of sight.

My arm was hurting like fury, which perhaps made me faint, or it may have been Neer's pills that put me to sleep. Marty said the big basket changed hands several times, but none of this was in my memory, if it happened while I was conscious.

I did have a dream, though. It was about the boy with the Gurkha knife. In the dream he said something in plain English, to me: "There is no problem for you—come to Shanta Bhawan!"

9. *Paths of Service*

EVERYTHING AROUND ME WAS WHITE! I WAS LYING ON A white bed, looking at white ceiling and walls. A woman wearing a white cap and white dress was sitting at a white table, winding up strips of white gauze.

When the woman looked up, I saw she was really a girl, a Westerner. She looked about my age.

"Hi!" she exclaimed, jumping up from the table and coming over my way. "I'm Pat Kingston. My father met you in Chicago, and he'll be here in a little while. I'm supposed to ask you what you would like to have for breakfast."

"Steak," I said. "Or chicken, or pie, or hamburgers. What time is it?"

"My goodness, you are starving!" she exclaimed. "It's ten o'clock and your friends were up hours ago. In fact Neer and the men have started back to Katmandu."

"And left me here all alone?" I asked.

"What do you mean, alone?" she asked. "I'm here, and a lot of other nice people!" (I liked her!) "And those two boys stayed, too, to go back with you," she added. "I'll get your breakfast."

I was a little curious about everything, but more hungry than curious.

When she got back with a big tray of eggs and oatmeal and toast and everything we take for granted back home, it was a feast—a banquet.

"This is special," she said, as she put the tray down on the table by my bed. "We don't give everybody the royal treatment. Can you manage all right with that arm?"

While she talked, she put a pillow behind me. It was a little awkward doing everything left handed, but I could manage. It wasn't hard at all to get used to having breakfast brought in, and to be waited on by somebody like Pat!

"You know, I don't think your arm is really so bad," she said. "But Miss Sudershenam—she's the head nurse here—says you'll have to be perfectly quiet. That's why they didn't put you over at our house, where the boys are staying."

I asked if this was a hospital, and she said it was only a dispensary.

"We don't have a doctor yet, and we don't have much room either. The patients may be coming in, although this isn't regular clinic day. I hope you don't mind."

I certainly didn't, and while I was eating my breakfast one did come with the nurse. It was a woman with a baby. The baby looked pretty sick to me, and the mother seemed to feel that way, too. She wasn't wearing a headshawl, so I could get a good look at her face. Her eyes looked terrified.

"It's the first time she's been here," Pat told me in a low voice, although I knew that the woman couldn't understand. "She was afraid to come, but I guess the baby is so bad now that she's afraid not to! But if anybody can help that baby, Miss Sudershenam can. She's wonderful."

When the nurse had finished looking at the baby, and given her a little package of medicine, the woman almost ran out of the room. After that the nurse came over to my bed, and Pat introduced us. She smiled and bowed, but didn't speak. Pat laughed, as she shook her head.

"Sudy won't try her English when there's a strange American here," she said. "But she speaks English perfectly well!"

Miss Sudershenam made another quick bow, said something that might have been "excuse me," and went racing out as if she had important business to attend to.

"Oh dear, I've embarrassed her!" Pat exclaimed. "Father is always warning me about that. She's shy. But Sudy's the best nurse in Nepal. That's really the truth!"

I asked her then how long I'd be staying here. She thought it would be two or three days.

"We sent a radio message," she said. "The helicopter is coming Friday to pick you up."

"Does my father know all about this, too?" I asked.

"Yes, but he's not worried," she assured me. "My father radioed that you were all right, and he wired back to tell you to be sure to 'get a story!' What did that mean?"

That was Dad for you! I explained about our news lingo. "Dad's going to let me write for his column," I said, trying not to act too cocky. "And about flying—the only thing that's bad is missing the hike. I hate to sort of change horses in the middle of the stream!"

"But you couldn't trek back," she insisted. "As it is they might have to break your arm all over again when you get to Shanta Bhawan."

"Shanta Bhawan!" I sat up straight and then yelled, "Ouch!" Pat quickly fixed the pillow again.

"What made you do that?" she asked. "You acted as if you'd seen a ghost. Have you been to Shanta Bhawan before?"

"Not exactly," I said, "but I have an interest in it."

She was a person you really liked to talk to. I told her about the blind boy at the hotel, and how Shanta Bhawan was something that seemed to keep coming up all the time, and how it was getting to mean more than just a hospital to me. I told her, too, how Dad had assigned me to write the story.

"So now you're going to be a patient there!" she exclaimed. "Isn't that neat! You can get a really good story, too, from the inside."

She thought about it for a minute, and then went on slowly, "You know, I believe most people do feel that way about Shanta Bhawan. I suppose you know how it got started, don't you?"

Mother had talked about it, but I'd forgotten the details.

"It'll come back when you get there," she told me. "But I do hope Dr. Robert Fleming and his wife, Dr. Bethel Fleming, will be there. They're the original ones who got the work started. And then Dr. Edgar Miller and his wife, Dr. Elizabeth, came soon afterward."

"What a lot of doctors!" I exclaimed.

"Not nearly so many as they need," she said. "And, of course, Dr. Robert isn't a medical doctor. He's an ornithologist, like your friend Marty's father and mother."

"Nepal must be a happy hunting ground for bird and flower people," I commented.

"For all kinds of scientists," she added. "And government people, religious researchers—you'd be surprised how many people get all the way over here to the center even. You'd think we were hidden clear away from the world, wouldn't you?"

"But actually you're famous!" I told her about how my mother's missionary society had been interested and how she wanted me to see Ama Kmu. "Mother said it was only a quarter of an inch from Katmandu!"

"And six days' trek over the mountains!" she laughed. "But it's only about an hour by helicopter, so she wasn't so wrong at that! The 'copter lands right on the school ground here in the village, and it's for emergencies, like you!"

"What church does the mission belong to?" I asked.

"No special one," she said. "It's Christian, but no special kind, like Methodist or Mennonite. It's several of them working together."

"Well," I said, "I guess you're the first missionary I ever saw out on his job location."

"But I'm not a missionary," she said. "Or not exactly.

My father and mother are, and Miss Sudershenam, of course, and the other adults. I'm just a missionary's kid!"

"Miss Sud—" I couldn't pronounce it. "But she—she isn't an American, is she? She didn't speak English."

Pat shook her head. "No, she's from India."

India—that seemed odd! "Are there missionaries from all over?"

"From lots of places," she said. "The two agricultural missionaries are from India, and one of the teachers is from England, and another one is from Canada. Oh yes, and there's a new Japanese nurse, coming in a week or two!"

"Missionaries from India!" I exclaimed. "And Japan! That's certainly something to think about!"

She laughed. "We've got heaps of things to think about here!" she said. "And Dad's coming in right now, so you'll soon have a lot more! The boys are with him, so I'd better take your tray out."

She left as they came in, and it was great to see them all again. It was like ten years since I'd gotten in that basket and we'd started from the Gurkha house! Marty and Rama seemed to be having a swell time, and Mr. Kingston looked just the same as he had in Chicago, except for his clothes.

"It's been so long since Chicago that I thought you'd look a lot older," I said, and he laughed.

"You're the one who's been through the aging experiences," he said. "After all, I didn't meet a bear, and you did!"

"Because he came by helicopter, that's why!" Marty said.

"Guess what, Dave, you can fly here! You can't come in a car or a train, but you can fly! Can you beat it?"

Rama had very little to say and seemed even more thoughtful than usual. But Marty couldn't keep still.

"Why, Dave," he exclaimed, "you just ought to get out and dig this place. I never knew missionaries did such useful things—even farming and school teaching. They're just like—just like good citizens!"

Pat had come back, just in time to hear that. She looked a little offended, but Mr. Kingston laughed as if he really liked what Marty said.

"You know, that's a compliment!" he said. "Not every missionary gets called a good citizen! I'm glad it shows!"

"It sure does!" Marty said enthusiastically. "Why, Dave, there's a dairy where they have cows and milk. And there's a school, and they even teach the grown-ups things about building houses and everything. There's not a preacher in the whole outfit, either, but they don't need any. It's a good idea, you know, to give people things like that, because if you do, then it's no trick at all to get them to become Christians!"

Pat looked even more put out this time, and I wished she could understand that Marty didn't mean a thing by all that talk. Of course, I did think Marty should have had better sense, but Mr. Kingston still didn't seem to be bothered. I could tell he liked both the boys, but especially Marty.

"I didn't say I wasn't a preacher, Marty," he corrected.

"I said I wasn't an ordained minister, and you shouldn't call me 'Reverend.' In a way everybody employed in this center is a preacher, because there are lots of ways of preaching, same as there are lots of ways of teaching. You might say we believe in the workshop method."

"Workshop?" Rama spoke at last. "I am confused, like Martin, about Christians, and I do not understand workshops."

"It means you do things instead of talking about them," Pat said. "We think there are certain ways Christians ought to live, too, and if you act that way, then you've said something to people. Isn't that right, Dad?"

"That's making it pretty simple," he said. "But it will do for the moment."

"And we've still got to go to the village market, you know," Marty said. "Rama, you'll have to go along to talk for me."

"And bargain for you," Rama said smiling. "We hope David will be well soon."

When the boys and Pat Kingston left, I felt a little lonesome. Mr. Kingston seemed to understand because he sat down in the chair to talk to me.

"Maybe it will help you to get a patient's-eye view of the center," he said. "It's too bad you can't move around yet, but Miss Sudershenam's word is law around here. Anyway, you can see most of the center and some of the village from this window, and I can interpret for you."

We both looked out. "If you were in good walking form,

it wouldn't take more than an hour for you to pace the whole thing. This is a small operation. It's the idea behind it that's big."

I could see the village, most of it, from where I lay, and it looked small, although I knew there were a lot of people crowded together there. It was as if several of those crowded narrow little streets of Katmandu had been lifted out of the city and set down here on this mountain side. There were the same little houses with balconies, almost close enough that a person could reach across the street to touch the balconies on the other side. I could see a few people, in clusters around what I thought must be the market place. And then I could see the school, with boys and girls outside right now. And up closer to the dispensary were the small farm buildings and a house where a family must live. Mr. Kingston pointed out the main office building and the one he said was the dairy. All the buildings were of mud. It wasn't, as Mr. Kingston said, a very big operation.

"The idea of different kinds of churches working here doesn't bother me," I began. "I'm used to Baptists and Presbyterians and all of them working together. What's the word—ecu—?"

"Ecumenical," he helped me out.

"Yes, I've heard a good deal about that from Mother," I said. "But the thing that surprises me—I mean one thing I wasn't expecting was to have missionaries here from—well—"

"India?" he asked.

"Yes, and Japan," I said.

"Why not?" he asked me.

I couldn't think why.

"No reason," I said finally. "Only India and Japan are the places we're always sending missionaries *to*. It makes you wonder if Nepal will be sending missionaries to America one of these days!"

"It might be a very good idea," he said seriously. "The church, wherever it is in the world, ought to obey the command to go out and teach the gospel. Many in America could learn from some of the Nepalese Christians!

"But returning to the point you're making, we've found that a group of committed Christians from many countries, working together in a service project, is an efficient and satisfying way of demonstrating a fundamental Christian belief."

And then I came to that other question.

"I keep remembering what Marty mentioned about 'getting people to be Christians,' " I said. "Of course, anybody knows that's *not* the whole idea—and yet when you get right down to it—is that what you do here?"

Mr. Kingston fiddled with a pencil for a while and then he said, "Dave, I wonder if you'd like to hear the story of how this little place came to be. It's a long story, but you can stop me any time you wish. And, of course, I'm open to questions."

"I'm with you," I said.

"You know how the revolution of 1950 suddenly opened

the doors of Nepal to the world," Mr. Kingston began. "Well, the direction of life in Nepal changed from looking backward to looking forward, and this was not just in Katmandu but throughout the country to the farthest fastnesses. Every aspect of life was affected—people, land, natural resources, health and education, government, foreign relations. It was an awakened country, taking its place in today's world.

"And it was this country into which the Christian church came. Sometimes, you know, it's Christianity that makes the revolution. This time the change had already come, and our problem, as we saw it, was to find the best way for Christian people to help in creating the new Nepal and, if possible, helping it develop in the Christian way.

"Our study showed first that 90 per cent of the people were farmers living in scattered villages in the mountains, valleys, and plains. Only 5 per cent of the people could read. We found that living conditions were primitive, social institutions were simple and provincial, and the people were poor. Summing it up, they were living in the Middle Ages, not ready for the new Nepal that was coming into being. We found that they had the same struggles men have everywhere—for food, health, shelter."

"How did you know where to begin?" I asked.

"We decided that our way of working was through education, not necessarily in the area of books, but more in the area of such basic needs as food, health, and shelter. These came first, and they all came together.

"That was how we drew up the plans for the community service program. We looked for Christians who were nurses, doctors, teachers, farmers, all consecrated people who could relate their work and their teaching to their religious faith. So, in the life of the whole person, with all his needs and hopes and dreams, we would try to create, in this one area, the new Nepal."

"Sort of a little new Nepal," I contributed.

"The government thought it was a good enough idea to try, and gave us permission to begin in this district here, where there are 190,000 people living in the Middle Ages!

"Three of us, an American, an Englishman, and a Nepalese, came out here together," he continued, "and I think the best thing we did was to make sure that we came with the approval and at the invitation of the people themselves. From the beginning we all worked together."

"How did you set up shop?"

"First we used a tent, then a bamboo thatch house, and then a stone and mud building like the one we are in now. The first school was a dozen boys gathered under a tree. Now there are about two hundred students, including adults as well as children. The first health work was done for a mother who brought her burned baby to be treated. The first agricultural project began with a gift of fifty fruit trees from a friend in Katmandu.

"Today a runner shuttles back and forth with the business pouch. He manages a crew of dozens of porters, like the men who came on your trek, and they bring in supplies of medicines, tools, books, seeds. Did you know, for instance, that Bir and his twin brother had between them about a hundred pounds of medical supplies for this clinic?"

So that was what they had in those big bundles!

"With the growing activity in this community, the government finally opened a post office," Mr. Kingston continued. "Recently they have started construction of an airfield a few miles away, and meanwhile the helicopter makes weekly trips for emergencies."

He stopped, leaving me breathless, just listening.

"What happens if you should leave?" I asked finally.

"If we're doing our job well," he said, "then we who started it ought to be able to leave. And I hope, when that time comes, we'll find the job is good. But we have a little more to do first.

"You see, so far, this has all been largely in terms of simple physical needs. But the idea, the great idea with which we began, is ever so much bigger. Ama Kmu is only a remote village in the mountains. The community service program is small, just like a little cork, bobbing on the waves of an ocean of mountains. But it is a place where a group of people from many parts of the world join together in a struggle to discover the truth and demonstrate it—the truth that man's search for the good life is not only a physical but a spiritual one and that, in the end, it has no other except a religious solution. The solution lies in obedience to God's law, and in the grace of God's gospel. Here is the abundant life that all men seek.

"Maybe I'm coming back to your question, or Marty's, right here. This is the way we choose to work and to preach, Dave, through trying to be true brothers and sisters in this community, serving and sharing together, facing life's problems together, and seeking to come together into what we believe is the final resolution and solution—the Lordship of Jesus Christ. That's the story."

He stopped again, and I couldn't think of anything to say or ask. To be honest, I couldn't understand all he'd just finished saying, either, but I tried to remember, because I wanted to think about it later on.

"I'm afraid I've lost you," he said.

"Maybe," I said. "But I'll keep thinking. I wanted to ask you about missionaries. It seems as though almost anybody can be a missionary. I mean—you need to do—well, everything that people need to do."

He smiled. "That's right. Modern-day missions need writers, journalists, columnists, novelists—all kinds of writers, just in case you're wondering."

"That's just what I was wondering!" I said. "And then another thing. It takes a lot of patience, doesn't it! Like that woman, who wouldn't come to the dispensary until maybe too late, because she was afraid. It takes people a long time to learn—even about physical things."

"It sure does," he agreed. "And some never learn."

"And it takes even longer for them to—sort of catch the idea of—God's law. You know you can understand about being hungry and you can understand—well, even about being a good citizen. But to tie it up to God, that takes a long time, a lot of patience."

"It takes a lot of patience on God's part," Mr. Kingston said, "to wait for all of us, including you and me, to see the connection! It hurts to think how, most of the time, God's gifts go begging! And it sometimes frightens me to think what would happen, if God should ever lose his patience!"

10. "*We Hold These Truths*"

IT WAS LUCKY FOR ME THAT AFTER PATIENTLY HOLDING ME down for two days in the dispensary, even Miss Sudershenam decided I was not much of an invalid. She cautiously gave me permission to walk around a little with Marty and Rama. "Walk quietly," she said.

It only took a little over an hour to go the length and breadth of the Community Center, even quietly, and also to cover a good part of the village.

Back at the dispensary, where I'd found myself that first day, we saw the waiting room full of sick people, most of them mothers with their babies. We saw how the women looked at the nurse, and even at Pat, who is only my age, as if those two had magic power. In a way, of course, they did, and I could see how there was something beyond medicine that they were able to give. It had to do with faith, although religion was never mentioned in words, so far as I know. And, of course, it was the Christian faith. It was the kind of work Jesus did, and it was being done the same way he did much of his work, by living example.

The woman I had seen the first day came back with her baby. I could hardly believe it was the same one; it was well! I remembered how scared the mother had been to come the first time, and how she'd had to decide to trust these people. I wondered if she sensed what I did: that there was more than medicine involved.

Marty was especially interested in the dispensary, because he thinks he might be a doctor later on. But he said he never realized before what a different kind of job it is taking care of sick people in a place like this and being a doctor in a big city office. "Any good doctor likes his patients and wants them to get well," he said. "And, of course, any doctor likes to cure sickness or he wouldn't go in for that kind of work. But there's something extra that doctors are doing here in Nepal, and they seem to have some special reason for doing their work," he added as we left the dispensary.

When we got outside we forgot all about doctors and why some do things one way and some do them another way. There was something strange about Ama Kmu that helped us talk pretty honestly among ourselves about all kinds of things. Being together in a Christian center, among mostly Buddhist and Hindu mountain people, made each one of us more aware of his own faith and more eager to ask questions about it and to know it better.

The time when we really dug in the most came on our last night at Ama Kmu. It was right after supper. Pat and Mr. Kingston suggested we go out to watch the sun set beyond the snowy peaks. Maybe our deepest sharing came then, because we knew it might be our last night together for our whole lives. Rama and Marty and I had become mighty close to one another.

Anyway, there we were: Marty, a Jew; Rama, a Hindu; and Pat and Mr. Kingston and I, Christians. We looked out together across the valley, and even though I'd been looking at them since my first night in Nepal, I still felt a shiver in my spine whenever I saw those jagged rocks and cliffs, and the snow-covered peaks, ruby colored from the red sky. It made me feel as if I were smack up against something majestic and significant, something far more important than the things that seemed important yesterday or last week.

It was so still it almost seemed noisy. A bird swooped across the valley and alighted somewhere on the far side. Nothing else stirred.

"I wonder how he can do it—flying like that!" Marty exclaimed.

"It makes you think of God," I practically whispered.

Marty looked as if his mind were far, far away. Rama looked as if he were in a trance.

Suddenly Marty blurted out, "Rama, there's one thing I don't understand about Nepal. Why do some of the Buddhist temples have shrines in them to Hindu gods?"

Rama recovered quickly and answered calmly, "Hinduism is a very ancient religion in this part of the world. The Gautama Buddha himself was born in Nepal and Buddhism grew out of Hinduism, so it is quite natural for Buddhism and Hinduism to exist together here."

"Just from looking around in your temples, I get the idea that Hindus have lots of gods," I said.

"I read somewhere that it's up in the thousands or even millions," Pat added in a very impressed tone.

"Yes, the uneducated people believe in many, many gods," Rama said, "but the three main gods are: Brahma, the Creator; Vishnu, the Preserver; and Siva, the Destroyer."

"Aren't there three persons in your religion, too?" Marty asked, turning to the Kingstons and me.

"Yes, but the Christian Trinity is different from the three gods of Hinduism, I think," I answered quickly. "It's awfully difficult to explain, but first, there's the Father, who creates everything."

"He's the same as our God," added Marty.

"The second person in the Trinity is Jesus," Pat went on. "He really lived on earth. Just as we think of God as the Father, so we think of Jesus as the Son, and as the Savior of the world."

"And then there is the Holy Spirit," I added. "That is just like saying that God is always in the world—all around us and inside us, too, helping us know and do what is right."

"Dave, you might as well be a Hindu," Marty concluded,

"and, Rama, you might as well be a Christian, for all I can see."

"Well, I'm afraid that is where you are wrong, Marty," Mr. Kingston interrupted. "There really is a great difference between what Hindus believe and what Christians believe. See if you can explain it to him, Dave," Mr. Kingston said to me.

My mind was a blank. I tried to remember what we had said that first day when we looked out of the dispensary window. It all seemed clear then. Finally I hedged by saying, "Mr. Kingston, I don't really see how I can explain the difference between Rama's religion and mine, because I really don't know anything about his religion." I felt that really let me off the hook. I was, in fact, quite pleased with myself. But not for long, for Rama volunteered a very simple explanation. He said that Hindus seek salvation through a discovery of their true selves.

"Well," I said, "I'm sure there is a difference, but I don't think I can explain exactly what it is."

Mr. Kingston came to my rescue. "Our Christian idea of sin is really different from that of the Hindu religion in several ways. For one thing, we Christians don't so much seek salvation as accept it. God gives it to us. What's more, while Hindus seek salvation from life, we may be said to look for salvation from death—that is, from spiritual death, sin, and aimlessness."

"I'd like to hear more about what this 'salvation from life' means," I put in.

Rama provided the answer. "We believe that when the body dies the soul lives on, taking some other form. The next state of existence, therefore, depends on how a person lived this life. For example, in my next incarnation I might be an outcaste or even a fly or a worm, if I am bad in this life; or I might rise to be a very highly respected man next time if I live the right way in this life. This is the way things go on and on and on, but we all hope—we Hindus, I mean—that some day we will escape all of this. We call it nirvana—when you don't have to live any more lives."

"But what do you do then, when you don't live any more lives?" I asked.

"Nothing, really," came Rama's reply. "You can't do anything or think anything or plan anything or feel anything, because you *aren't* anything. You don't exist any more—not as a separate person, anyway."

"But why?" I asked. I had more questions than anybody, it seemed. "*Why* don't you want to go on living? If life is good instead of bad, why do you want it to end? Our New Testament, you know. . . ." I caught my mistake at once and added, "or maybe you don't know, . . . talks about everlasting life."

Suddenly Pat steered the conversation away from Rama to Marty. "I'd like to know what Jews say about salvation."

"I guess our idea is different from both Hinduism and Christianity," Marty replied. "For us the main thing is obeying the laws of God. For one thing, there are the Ten Commandments—and then there are a lot of other laws, too, about how to live. Above all, there's the moral law: doing right things rather than wrong things."

"I think this is fascinating," said Pat. "Do you see what we're really saying? We're saying that the Hindus and Jews try to work for what they want; they try to live a certain way so they can get the benefit of salvation. But Christians don't work for their salvation; God *gives* it to them. Is that right, Dad?"

"Yes, that's about it," replied Mr. Kingston.

Pat's a missionary's daughter, so maybe she should know about such things, but I was sure glad she was around. And with the glint of the setting sun on her hair, I thought she looked even prettier than she had in her hospital uniform.

"Well, anyway," Rama said, sending my thoughts back to the discussion, "I can't think we're really so far apart. Sure, we have differences; but it's like being on different paths. They all lead to the top of the mountain—what does it matter which path you take?"

"It sure mattered to me what path I was on when I fell," I pointed out. "But let me ask about what Pat was saying a moment ago. I mean about people working or not working to find their salvation. Would it also be true, then, to say that in Christianity God doesn't simply give us laws or tell us what to do—he himself does something? He loves people so much that even when they break his laws he sends Jesus to be their Savior? And isn't this what Christians mean when they talk about the good news, or the gospel?"

No one answered. Of course, I hadn't asked any person

in particular. So I went on; by now ideas were coming to me faster than I could form them into sentences.

"If I get the picture right, that's what really makes Christians go places and do things in the world. Like some of them traveling from India and Canada and the States and England to this place here, Ama Kmu. Missionaries don't come here in order to work their way up to a better life, but simply because God has been good to them and so they want to do good, too. Right, Mr. Kingston?"

"Right you are, Dave," came the reassuring reply. "Of course, if you asked ten different Christians about this you'd get ten different answers, but they'd really be saying just one thing: God loves us, so we love, too.

"And the way we show our love is by using our talents in service. Some Christians, who are doctors and nurses and lab technicians, can offer the gift of healing. Some can offer the important gift of education; still others can share improved farming methods. Whatever we have is not for ourselves, but for others; that's how we do God's will and show our gratitude to him for all his gifts to us."

By now the sun had set and the moon was beginning to show in the darkening sky. After a moment of silence Marty said, "Boy, this sure is a lot to think about. I'm not sure I understand it all, and I'm not sure I exactly go along with what I do understand, but I sure want to think about it some more when I get back home."

Mr. Kingston reached out an arm and laid it across Marty's shoulder.

"I see we didn't quite lose you, Buster," he said. I got the idea that he thought a lot of Marty, as I did, too.

Rama hadn't said a word for quite a while, and I wondered if this talk about Christianity had perhaps offended him. But the next thing he said made me feel better.

"All of this raises questions that I must think about also," he said slowly. "Certainly I'd like to know more about both your religions, but there is much about my own that I should know better, too. Hindus are likely to observe many customs without thinking about their significance. But I believe that we have made a beginning by meeting here, in just this way here on the mountain, seeking truth."

"That's exactly what I was trying to say," I exclaimed. "Only you say it better—more like a poet!"

On the way back to the center, Marty and I walked together, a little behind the others. Mr. Kingston shone his flashlight back now and then to help us see. We didn't talk much. Marty was thoughtful, and all of a sudden he let out a sigh.

"You know, Dave," he said, "Ama Kmu isn't like other places. All this love and service, and all our talk tonight about what God is like and how he wants us to live—it's good, isn't it? I think it's real good. But where can you have it, Dave, except in Ama Kmu?

"Tomorrow we'll be in Katmandu. In a couple of weeks you'll be back in Chicago. In about six weeks I'll be getting back to Toronto. And you know, back there where you and

I live people will be talking about war, and communism, and exams, and all that. It seems like everybody is afraid, and everybody is grabbing. What do you make of it?"

I didn't know. I couldn't answer.

It was quite dark now, but always beyond our darkness we could see the beam of Mr. Kingston's flashlight. It didn't seem right that beyond Ama Kmu the world was so full of all kinds of problems. Was there nothing good, nothing worth looking forward to beyond this little place?

Then something half remembered came to the top of my mind.

"Why," I said. "There is no problem for you. Come to Shanta Bhawan!"

"Are you nuts?" Marty asked.

"No," I said. "I was just thinking."

11. *Farewell to Ama Kmu*

THE MORNING WE TOOK OFF FOR KATMANDU, IT SEEMED everybody in Ama Kmu gathered down at the schoolground to see us off. I asked Pat Kingston if she'd ever gotten used to the way the Nepalese always make a party of these things, and she said she had it figured out. "They make it a party," she said, "so it won't be a funeral." Anyway, it was one of the nicest customs, and Pat said it was the same way all over the Orient.

The Ama Kmu schoolground was not exactly the O'Hare Airport in Chicago and, of course, a helicopter can't compare with a 707 jet.

Our funny little craft, looking like a skeleton with a great big nose, heaved and shuddered and finally yanked itself away from the ground and lifted straight up into the sky. I looked down at the crowd of folks waving, and for a while I could distinguish different ones: Pat, Mrs. Kingston, Miss Sudershenam, and some of the villagers. The schoolteacher's red scarf really stood out for quite a while. Finally everybody seemed to melt together into a lump that grew smaller and smaller until we couldn't even see the waving. At last we were four people in a pumpkin shell (five counting the pilot), suspended in the sky.

Marty's voice broke into my thinking like a message from outer space. "You look scared, Dave," he said.

I jumped, and they all laughed. "So do you," I told him.

He nodded. "I am," he admitted. "And what I don't understand is, why this seems scary when you don't even notice being 35,000 feet above the ocean in a big plane—even in the middle of the night."

"Maybe that's it," I said. "You can't see where you are when you are that high."

"And they keep coming around with newspapers and coffee and food and everything," Marty went on. "It's just like being at home. Most of the time you don't even know you are moving, and you can't hear much noise."

We certainly could hear the noise the helicopter was making; we could feel it jiggle, too.

"Makes me feel as if all this means something—you know, something important!" Marty said.

I knew what he meant. Rama had a strange look on his face, too, as if he were thinking of something.

Mr. Kingston noticed it, too. "Is it a poem?" he asked, so softly I could barely hear. Perhaps he didn't want to break into anything Rama might be thinking, but Rama heard.

"I am thinking of my country," he answered slowly. "And the helicopter. Today we travel from Ama Kmu to Katmandu in one hour. Last week, we traveled that same distance in six days. This is the new Nepal. We are flying into the future." Then he added modestly, "That is what my father says."

"Spinning into the future, I'd say!" Marty exclaimed.

"And this is an exciting thing to you?" Mr. Kingston asked Rama.

"My father says that it is both good and bad," Rama answered. "Perhaps it is a danger to our minds. Perhaps speed is too strange for our people. . . ."

Mr. Kingston nodded thoughtfully.

"There is danger in this sudden awakening," he agreed, "but there is great opportunity, too—if we can keep calm, and if we can have confidence."

"Courage!" Rama exclaimed. "I think we need much courage. You see, it is as though we had slept here through centuries, behind our closed doors, and now, waking, we find all the world has gone far beyond." He thought again. "We must learn—you must teach us—very fast!"

"We must learn together," Mr. Kingston corrected. "You

and I are all a part of the new Nepal—the airport, Ama Kmu, Shanta Bhawan—"

"We'll soon be at Shanta Bhawan, too," Marty interrupted cheerfully. "I hope they tell Dave his wing is O.K." I hoped so too. "By the way, Dave, you've never been there yet, have you?"

I began to say that I hadn't and then stopped. "Not exactly," I said. "But in a way—yes, I have!"

"What do you mean, in a way you have?" Marty demanded.

I hesitated and then told them about what happened in the hotel the day we arrived, and about the way the blind boy's face lighted up.

"I knew all the time that Shanta Bhawan is a hospital," I said. "But it seemed to be more than that, and every time it comes up again, I keep feeling that it—well, it means something. It seems to mean all of Nepal to me. The friendliness, the beauty, the kindness of everybody, strangers and all—I just put it all together and think 'Shanta Bhawan!' "

Marty looked puzzled, but Mr. Kingston seemed to understand, as Pat had back at the Community Center.

"*Bhawan* means 'home' or 'dwelling place,' " he said. "Many people feel that Shanta Bhawan is indeed a home of a special kind, and far more than just a hospital. There are so many things I could tell you about it and there are many more things you will read in the books and papers. Some things you will see for yourself. You ought to make a story of it, Dave."

I didn't mention to him just then that Dad had suggested that very thing. About then we realized that the helicopter had begun to make a different kind of noise and to jiggle in a different way. We were beginning to come down.

Even while we were on the way down, I was thinking,

into the city, lots of people again, lots of trouble, sickness, misunderstanding, noise!

"Out of yesterday into today," Rama said softly.

"Out of the sky and back to earth!" Marty answered cheerfully. "I guess our folks will be glad to see us, all right! But it'll seem odd to be in Katmandu, won't it?"

It was hard to believe when we bumped onto the ground that we were actually right at the door of the place I'd been waiting so long to see. We got a hazy look from the helicopter at the big white building, another Rana palace, that was the hospital. Then the door was opened, and there were all the folks—Marty's father and mother, and a whole crowd of the Prasad family, and my father. I saw Dad before he saw me, and it made me feel bad to see how worried he looked, when he didn't know I could see him.

"Hi!" I yelled to him. "Didn't we meet some place?" (That's what we always say.) Then he saw me and grinned.

"Hi, Big Explorer," he said. "You did it the hard way, I see."

"My new name is Scoop," I responded. "I'm full of stories. So when do I start work?"

"You've already started," Dad said. By that time he'd gotten through the crowd and was squeezing my shoulder, the one that didn't hurt. "But right now you've got a date at the hospital. Get out your notebook, Scoop, because you've landed right on top of a story!"

I had come to Shanta Bhawan!

12. *Come to Shanta Bhawan!*

This Is Our World

Today's newspaper column is written by a guest—David C. Brown, Jr., the fourteen-year old son of the regular contributor to this page. Young David's assignment was the Shanta Bhawan Hospital in Nepal. He did his research the hard way, by breaking his right arm and being taken to the hospital for treatment.—D.C.B.

KATMANDU, Nepal.—After traveling sixty miles over the Himalayas, a helicopter dropped me and some companions onto the grounds of Shanta Bhawan, in this city of wonders.

Shanta Bhawan is a hospital, and Bhawan is the Nepali word for "home" or "dwelling place." This was a kind of homecoming for me, because this place has been a goal of mine ever since the day we arrived in Nepal. I came via a long trek to Ama Kmu Community Center, which, like Shanta Bhawan, is a project of the United Mission to Nepal.

The people with whom I flew back from Ama Kmu were not the only arrivals at Shanta Bhawan. Others had come, not by helicopter, but on foot or, strapped in a basket, were carried on somebody's shoulders. Two men came crawling on the ground. These people were sick, many with diseases I had barely heard of.

One man, who had difficulty walking, shook hands with all us Westerners. I noticed that his hands were deformed and that the right one had several fingers missing. Nevertheless, he shook hands with everybody and wished us "long life and many children."

One of my companions from the helicopter explained the handshaking, which is not a Nepalese custom. "This man has recently been cured of leprosy," he said. "He doesn't need to stay at the hospital, but he likes to come to Shanta Bhawan to meet the helicopter whenever it comes in and to greet Westerners in the Western way."

From that introduction everything that has happened here has made this place an answer to the many questions that I've had about this amazing country and also about the program of the United Mission to Nepal, which has an important role in this newly opened country.

Somebody has said that Shanta Bhawan is a small reflection of the world-wide mission idea. Or that it is a little United Nations with the cross for its symbol. It is more than a hospital, because it reaches out through clinics and other services into the whole valley and beyond the valley. It is operated by people from many different church groups and many countries. It is approved by the Government of Nepal, and part of its service is to train Nepalese for various medical professions.

Shanta Bhawan was an early project of the United Mission to Nepal and still is the largest. Other mission projects include a girls' school in the Katmandu Valley, a hospital in the nearby city of Bhadgaon, and another hospital in the Tansing area of Nepal. The work of the Community Center at Ama Kmu, in the Gurkha District, is fundamental education, literacy, farming, medicine, and community planning.

The work of the United Mission is the result of the "discovery" of Nepal by Dr. Robert Fleming, an ornithologist, who went into the newly-opened country to hunt rare birds. His wife, Dr. Bethel Fleming, found herself having a busman's holiday, treating sick people all along the way.

At the invitation of the Government of Nepal and with the help of several missionary societies, medical work at Shanta Bhawan was begun in 1954. Today eighteen different churches and missions contribute to its support. King Mahendra visits the hospital sometimes, and so does Sir

Edmund Hillary. One of the recent emergency cases at the hospital was one of Hillary's Sherpa guides who, like me, broke an arm.

There are several resident physicians at Shanta Bhawan, but they need many more. Counting clinic patients in the villages, they treat about forty thousand cases a year.

Right now Dr. Robert and Dr. Bethel Fleming are on leave, and the physicians in charge are Dr. Edgar Miller and his wife, Dr. Elizabeth Miller. These American missionaries call themselves old, because they have grandchildren back home, but "old" is the wrong word for them. Dr. Elizabeth told me that all their lives they had wanted to serve as medical missionaries overseas, but they had waited until their children grew up. It seems as though Nepal was waiting, too, because the Millers came not long after the country was open.

The Millers are sort of Nepalese by adoption, because they have adopted a little Nepalese girl, Bishnu, who is probably six years old, although nobody knows exactly. She was brought in with club feet when she was a tiny baby. She is well now and speaks enough English to tell people she is part American. I guess that is the way I feel about Nepal, only in reverse. I feel as if I partly belong to Nepal.

The people here don't understand how Dr. Edgar and Dr. Elizabeth can do so much work without becoming tired. One of the boys said maybe they were special friends of God! I asked Dr. Elizabeth if she would give me a description of a typical day, but she said there was no such thing.

All days are one emergency after another, and the only thing they can be sure of is surprises.

For the missionaries at the hospital, every morning begins with a Scotch bath, breakfast, and morning worship. One of the nurses told me that it is amazing what a difference it makes to go to church when your church is a minority in a country. After worship there are hospital rounds.

I went around with Dr. Edgar this morning. Every single bed is taken today, but that is not unusual. There are about one hundred beds, or maybe a few more. The overflow patients are put on mattresses on the floor between the beds, or in the hallways. In one bed I saw two brothers.

Dr. Elizabeth and Dr. Edgar also go out to clinics in the villages, and sometimes as many as two hundred patients come to a clinic. At Shanta Bhawan they have special leprosy and cholera clinics, too. Every once in a while there is a cholera epidemic.

Shanta Bhawan is like Katmandu's Royal Hotel in one way. It is a Rana palace, or rather two palaces close together, which the mission rents. There are lots of courtyards and gardens, and I kept getting lost among them. The nurses live in what used to be the quarters for the Rana wives, and the doctors live in apartments in a bungalow.

One thing that interested me was the long building at the back of the hospital grounds. This building is broken up into cubicles, and each cubicle has a little fireplace. Patients' families stay in these and do the cooking for their own relatives. It is quite a neat arrangement, because the families become acquainted with the hospital and keep the patients from getting scared and homesick. Mothers can sleep in the wards with their children, too, if they wish.

Of course, most of the patients at Shanta Bhawan are poor, and it is interesting to see what they bring as payment for the services. Some carry chickens under their tunics, and some bring eggs, or even garlands of flowers. Nepal is a country of flowers.

There are rich patients, too, because anyone may go to Shanta Bhawan. My friend, Marty Rosen, had an emergency appendectomy several months ago. To hear him tell it, he had quite an exciting time, being carried up and down the steps to and from the operating room. There is no elevator in all Nepal.

My friend Rama Prasad, a Hindu, told me that his youngest sister was born in the hospital. This was shortly after Shanta Bhawan opened, and several of his uncles were quite angry, because it was a Christian hospital. But this year one of his cousins, the daughter of the angriest uncle, is taking nurse's training at the hospital.

There are some problems, too, that we do not have in the United States. For one thing, if a patient seems very sick, his family is apt to take him down to the sacred Baghmati River, so he can put his feet in the water and have his sins washed away before he dies. Removing him from a sick bed might very well make the patient die, even if he had a chance of getting better.

Dr. Elizabeth said also that they have trouble vaccinating against smallpox, because people think the goddess of smallpox might get angry if the doctors interfere with people catching it.

One of the worst problems, though, is getting blood for transfusions. For one thing, the people are afraid it might not be religious to exchange blood that way. Today a man was brought in, dying with peptic ulcer. He needed a transfusion. Twenty wailing members of his family came along with him, but not one would give blood for him. A Nepalese patient in the next room overheard the commotion, and said to his nurse, "You have saved my life. I am well now. Take my blood for the other sick one."

They did, and the ulcer patient is expected to recover. Dr. Elizabeth said it was the first time a Nepalese patient had offered to give his own blood for a stranger.

It seems to me that this is what makes the real difference between Shanta Bhawan and any other kind of government aid project. Besides medical help to a lot of people who would die without it, the mission demonstrates an idea that is new. For the first time, these folks see others actually giving their whole lives for strangers. At first, all this hard work without any financial profit does not make sense to most people here. (It does not make sense to most Americans, either.) But after a while some of the Nepalese begin to see that the real reward is bigger than money, and they begin to wonder what is behind it all. When the idea really hits home, it is a wonderful shock. Dr. Elizabeth says the idea of Christianity is always a shock, and it makes you change fast.

The last thing we did tonight was to go around and "put the family to bed," as Dr. Edgar said. He meant making sure that everybody was all right. So we walked through all the wards in the dim light and the quietness. There was a little soft talking; some of the relatives were in the wards with the patients and whispering to them. There was a little snoring, too, because some of the patients were already asleep.

When we came to the children, Dr. Edgar told me they wanted a story. I could not tell what the story was about, because it was in Nepali, but the little kids were as still as mice. When he stopped they all yelled in a chorus, which the nurse hushed right away. I guessed that they were saying, "Tell us another," and I was right. When we finally went out of the last ward, everything was hushed and still behind us.

So this is Shanta Bhawan—a hospital, a mission center, and a "dwelling place" of a special kind.

My father and I will soon be leaving this wonderful country. But in a way I will never leave Nepal, because I will take it with me, in my mind, all my life.

From now on I will read every newspaper looking for items about Nepal. I will wonder about the political situation here, and about King Mahendra and Queen Ratna, and what mountains are being climbed, and what the missionaries are doing.

I will remember some things my father said, too. He says that there is nothing more exciting than a country that has been completely shut up to suddenly become aware of the world outside.

Yesterday—illiteracy, disease, fear, and superstition. Today—schools, hospitals, a concerned government, questions about the old way of living, gradually opening doors. Tomorrow—an informed and healthy people, a free government, enlightened religious views, a wide-open gate to the world!

In so many ways Shanta Bhawan has come to mean this new Nepal to me. It is a hospital, and a mission center, but it is also an idea. It is the idea of service, and it comes with a religion whose living must also be its words.

I wish you could all come to Shanta Bhawan!

A WORD ABOUT THE FORMAT

TEXT SET IN LINOTYPE BASKERVILLE, 12 POINT LEADED 4 POINTS.
MANUFACTURED BY SOWERS PRINTING COMPANY, LEBANON, PENNSYLVANIA.
COVERS PRINTED BY AFFILIATED LITHOGRAPHERS, INC., NEW YORK.
TEXT PAPER, S. D. WARREN'S OLDE STYLE WOVE.
TYPOGRAPHIC DESIGN BY MARGERY W. SMITH.